Building a System of Tens

Casebook

A collaborative project by the staff and
participants of Teaching to the Big Ideas

Principal Investigators

Deborah Schifter
Virginia Bastable
Susan Jo Russell

with
Sophia Cohen
Jill Bodner Lester
Lisa Yaffee

Dale Seymour Publications®
Parsippany, New Jersey

This work was supported by the National Science Foundation under Grant Nos. ESI-9254393 and ESI-9050210. Any opinions, findings, conclusions, or recommendations expressed here are those of the authors and do not necessarily reflect the views of the National Science Foundation.

National Science Foundation

Additional support was provided by the Massachusetts Higher Education Coordinating Council and the Dwight D. Eisenhower Mathematics and Science Education Program.

Published by Dale Seymour Publications®, 299 Jefferson Road, Parsippany, NJ 07054.

Dale Seymour Publications® is an imprint of Addison Wesley Longman, Inc.

EXECUTIVE EDITOR: Catherine Anderson
PROJECT EDITOR: Beverly Cory
PRODUCTION/MANUFACTURING DIRECTOR: Janet Yearian
SENIOR PRODUCTION/MANUFACTURING COORDINATOR: Fiona Santoianni
DESIGN DIRECTOR: Phyllis Aycock
DESIGN MANAGER: Jeff Kelly
TEXT AND COVER DESIGN: Paula Shuhert
COMPOSITION: Joe Conte

ISBN 0-7690-0169-6
DS21961

3 4 5 6 7 8 9 10-ML-03 02 01

This product is printed
on recycled paper

Teaching to the Big Ideas

Developing Mathematical Ideas (DMI) was developed as a collaborative project by the staff and participants of Teaching to the Big Ideas, an NSF Teacher Enhancement Project.

PROJECT DIRECTORS   Deborah Schifter (EDC), Virginia Bastable (SummerMath for Teachers), Susan Jo Russell (TERC)

STAFF   Sophia Cohen (EDC), Jill Bodner Lester (SummerMath for Teachers), Lisa Yaffee (TERC)

PARTICIPANTS   Allan Arnaboldi, Lisa Bailly, Audrey Barzey, Julie Berke, Nancy Buell, Yvonne Carpio, Rose Christiansen, Ann Connally, Nancy Dostal, Marcia Estelle, Becky Eston, Trish Farrington, Victoria Fink, Gail Gilmore, Nancy Horowitz, Debbie Jacques, Marcy Kitchener, Rick Last, Eileen Madison, Joyce McLaurin, Rena Moore, Amy Morse, Deborah O'Brien, Marti Ochs, Anne Marie O'Reilly, Hilory Paster, Jessica Redman, Priscilla Rhodes, Margie Riddle, Jan Rook, Doug Ruopp, Sherry Sajdak, Cynthia Schwartz, Karen Schweitzer, Lisa Seyferth, Susan Bush Smith, Diane Stafford, Liz Sweeney, Nora Toney, Polly Wagner, Carol Walker, and Steve Walkowicz, representing the public schools of Amherst, Belchertown, Boston, Brookline, Lincoln, Newton, Northampton, Pelham, South Hadley, Southampton, Springfield, Westfield, and Williamsburg, Massachusetts, and the Atrium School in Watertown, Massachusetts.

VIDEO DEVELOPMENT   Susan Jo Russell, Judy Storeygard, David Smith, and Megan Murray (TERC), Jill Bodner Lester (SummerMath for Teachers)

CONSULTANTS, *BUILDING A SYSTEM OF TENS*   Deborah Ball and Magdalene Lampert (University of Michigan), Kathryn Irwin (University of Auckland), Terry Wood (Purdue University)

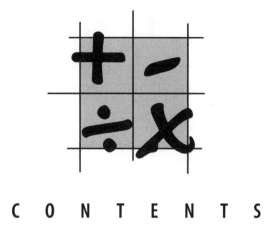

C O N T E N T S

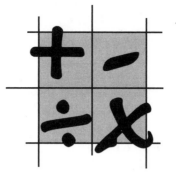

Introduction

Many elementary school teachers would rank place value and regrouping among the most important mathematics topics they teach each year. Many teachers would add that these topics are also troublesome for their students. Children frequently lose track of the notion that, say, the digit 4 in 45 stands for 4 tens, and many have a hard time remembering the correct procedures for calculating. Even sixth-grade teachers report that, although their students have been subtracting multidigit numbers for several years, some persist in always subtracting the smaller digit from the larger. For example, these students would claim that 342 minus 296 equals 154.

On the surface, it may seem mystifying that so many children, year after year, have such difficulty with these concepts. However, once we delve more deeply into an examination of the ideas underlying the base ten number system, we see that the ideas are, in fact, quite complex. When children are having difficulty learning the mathematics of the curriculum, the problem is not resolved by dismissing the children as "not made of the right stuff."

Indeed, the types of errors consistently made by many students have in them elements of logic. For example, when children write ninety-five as 905, they are applying to written numerals what they understand about spoken numbers. By listening to these children and trying to understand how their ideas make sense, we come to see more clearly the differences between the spoken and written systems for representing number; we also identify those ideas that the children need to work through.

What are the principles underlying our number system? How do children come to understand these principles? What are the connections that allow students to flexibly maneuver their way around the number system? One second-grade teacher, pondering these questions, wrote:

> Suppose children can tell you that one place is called the ones place, one the tens place, and so on, and that if you have 10 ones, you can't write it in the ones column alone, but you need to write it in the tens column as well, because 10 ones can be traded in for 1 ten and 0 ones. (Jeez, that sounds ridiculously complex!) This knowledge, in my experience, does not ensure that they are able to break numbers apart into tens and ones to make sense of adding double-digit numbers.

This casebook for the Developing Mathematical Ideas (DMI) seminar *Building a System of Tens* is designed to help groups of teachers, as well as others involved in elementary mathematics education, explore the structure of the base ten number system and the ways children come to understand it. The cases were written by elementary teachers, describing episodes from their own classrooms. The teacher-authors, who have themselves been working to understand the "big ideas" of the elementary mathematics curriculum, wrote these cases as part of their own process of inquiry. They came together on a regular basis to read and discuss one another's work.

The cases are grouped to present children in different classrooms who are working on similar mathematical issues related to the base ten structure of number. Through the cases, we can study children's initial ideas as they talk about how numbers are written and decomposed; the children's application of those ideas as they figure out how to add, subtract, multiply, and divide; and the ways children extend those ideas as they begin to think about decimal fractions.

In chapter 1, the cases look into three classrooms—one at sixth grade, the others second grade—to see how children think about adding and subtracting two-digit numbers. What are the various ways children naturally think about separating and combining numbers? And what is it that children must already understand in order to work with numbers in these ways?

This latter question motivates the rest of the casebook. In chapters 2–4, the cases present children working on basic concepts related to the use of tens and ones to structure numbers. After some of those concepts have been identified, the cases once again consider addition and subtraction. How children apply these basic concepts, and how these concepts can be extended to the work of the upper-elementary grades, is the focus of the chapters 5–7.

Chapter 8, the last in this casebook, is the essay "Highlights of Related Research." This essay summarizes some recent research findings that touch on the issues explored in the cases (chapters 1–7).

When this DMI seminar was first taught, many seminar participants reported that they had to learn how to read the cases.

> It's different from reading a story. I feel as if I've had to comb through each episode with a fine-toothed comb.

> I'm reading cases very slowly, and I'm writing down thoughts about what I'm seeing in the text.

Several teachers offered advice to other participants:

> This isn't easy to read. This isn't easy to think about. Give it time. Keep an open mind.

> Read all the cases in one chapter once and try to write down the mathematical issues raised in the cases. You might focus attention on two or three children in the episodes that interest you and really figure out the mathematical issues that these few children are facing. Try to really understand how the children are thinking. Here's another way to do it: After reading all the cases in a chapter, go over them again, looking for the common threads. What mathematical issues connect these cases together?

> Remember that these are glimpses of *real kids* dealing with *real* situations struggling to make sense of very difficult concepts. Pay particular attention to the *natural* ways students often solve problems.

> Begin with the chapter introduction. Then proceed case by case, paying close attention to what seems to be going on. Jot down questions as well as comments. It is sometimes helpful to reread the chapter introduction after each case. If possible, discuss the cases informally with other participants before the sessions. If you're unable to do any or some of the above, by all means don't *not* come to the study group!

As the seminar proceeds, you might talk to other participants about the ways they read the cases to prepare for seminar discussions.

C H A P T E R

1

Children's algorithms for adding and subtracting two-digit numbers

While participating in a professional development program one summer, Ann, a sixth-grade teacher, watched a videotape in which second graders presented their personal methods for solving two-digit addition and subtraction problems. For a problem such as 16 + 28, none of the children used the method most familiar to her: "6 + 8 is 14, so you put down the 4 and carry the 1. . . ." Instead, the children had ways of taking the numbers apart and recombining them to find the sum or difference. Ann and her colleagues (who were also viewing the video) had to work hard to understand what the children were doing, but they discovered that the children's methods did make sense.

When Ann met with her new group of sixth graders the following autumn, she was curious about whether these students, too, might have ways to solve problems that are different from the traditional "carry" and "borrow" procedures—and so she asked them. Sandra and Emily, two of Ann's colleagues who taught second grade at other schools, also asked their students to explain their thinking as they worked on addition and subtraction.

In these four cases, teachers Ann, Sandra, and Emily describe what they found as their students talked about their own ways of performing multidigit addition and subtraction. Readers are invited to take the time to make sense of what the children are doing. As you read the following cases, take notes on this question: Will the children's methods work for *any* pair of numbers?

Do my students think flexibly? Do I?

Ann

GRADE 6, OCTOBER

As a sixth-grade teacher, I was curious about how my students would solve problems if I could somehow erase from their minds the traditionally taught method. I was curious about how flexible my students would be in thinking about numbers: How would they manipulate them to solve a problem? I didn't believe they could really view addition differently from the way they had been taught for so many years. My hypothesis assumed that by the time students get to sixth grade, the traditional algorithm has been ingrained in them and would interfere with their abilities to think about math differently.

I gave all the students some addition problems orally and asked them to solve these without any physical aids: no paper, pencils, or manipulatives. Each problem involved some regrouping. Then I asked them to explore how they got their answers and to share their individual thinking with the class. In our class discussions, students shared their strategies

5

10

and responded to one another with comments and questions. To clarify
their thinking, they applied each suggested strategy to new problems.
Through this process, I made a number of discoveries.

Students Janae, Tom, Bert, and Betsy demonstrated four different
approaches to the same problem, 68 + 24 = ?

Janae's thinking:

$$68 + 24 = ?$$

$$60 + 20 = 80$$

$$8 + 4 = 12$$

$$80 + 12 = 92$$

Janae's first step was to add the tens and then the ones, moving from
left to right. This actually seemed to make the regrouping easier, because
of the zero in the 80. Why do we add the way we do, starting at the right
with the ones column? Isn't it easier to add from the left to the right?

Tom's thinking:

$$68 + 24 = ?$$

$$24 - 2 = 22$$

Take the –2 and add it to the 68 (68 + 2 = 70).

Add the 22 that was the answer from 24 – 2.

$$22 + 70 = 92$$

Many different questions arose about Tom's thinking, especially the
part where he subtracted 2. Where did the 2 come from? Why did 2 get
subtracted and not 3 or 4 or any other number? Was the –2 actually the
digit 2 in the number 24? Why did he subtract 2 from 24? Why didn't he
subtract something from the 68? Eventually, the class concluded that Tom
had manipulated the numbers, by taking away and adding on, to create a
"nice number" or a number with a zero in the ones. One student stated
that "zeros are good."

Bert's thinking:

$$68 + 24 = ?$$

Take the 24 and break it into smaller pieces.

$$24 = 5 + 5 + 5 + 5 + 4$$

Add the pieces onto the 68, one at a time, by counting up.

$68 + 5 = 73$

$73 + 5 = 78$

$78 + 5 = 83$

$83 + 5 = 88$

$88 + 4 = 92$

Bert's breaking up the problem was easily understood by the class, but many students stated that "keeping track" of the numbers would be difficult for them. It did work for Bert.

Betsy's thinking:

$$68$$
$$\underline{+\ 24}$$

$8 + 4 = 12$

Carry the 1 and add it to the $6 + 2$.

$1 + 6 + 2 = 9$

So the answer is 92.

Betsy's approach is the one I had predicted all my students would use: She pictured 68 and 24 written vertically and applied the traditional algorithm. However, I now feel that this strategy gives a limited view of what is really happening in an addition problem. Does Betsy sense that $6 + 2 + 1 = 9$ really is $60 + 20 + 10 = 90$?

When students answer problems in Betsy's way, we as teachers may presume they know more than they actually do. What do our students really understand when they successfully solve an addition problem the traditional way? Each manipulation of the individual digits seems discrete from every other, rather than part of a connected process. Asking students to give us what we want to hear rather than listening to what they're actually thinking can be very misleading when we are trying to judge what they truly understand.

My hypothesis was partially right and partially wrong. Some students did see addition in the traditional way, but many viewed it in ways that I could not have imagined. Students learned from each other that there are many ways to solve a single problem. Later, one student stated in her journal, "I didn't know there were so many ways to do addition." I didn't, either.

Creative thinking in subtraction

Ann

GRADE 6, OCTOBER

The traditional subtraction algorithm is a difficult procedure for many students to understand. Every year at the sixth-grade level, I see some students still struggling with the regrouping process in subtraction. They ask themselves, "When do I borrow? Is this where I cross out something? What if there is a zero in the column I want to take from? When do I stop borrowing?" They seem to be controlled by the numbers rather than controlling the numbers themselves. In this process, what the numbers mean or represent becomes secondary to manipulating the numbers, and students can quickly get lost.

As my students explored their own processes for doing mental math, they revealed fascinating thinking. This thinking is causing me to question why we teach the traditional subtraction algorithm. Is it really the most effective way to understand subtraction?

At the time of this episode, my students had already been investigating their mental math thinking processes. They had previously investigated how they did addition "in their heads." By now they were able to explain orally the addition process they used, and they were starting to record their steps in written form. The format of the subtraction investigation was similar to what we had done with addition. I gave all the students a subtraction problem orally and asked them to solve it without any physical aids: no paper, pencils, or manipulatives. Again, each problem involved some regrouping. Then I asked them to explore how they got their answers and to share their individual thinking with the class. In follow-up discussions, students responded to one another's strategies through comments and questions. As with addition, they applied each strategy to new problems to clarify their thinking. Through this process they shared the following approaches to the problem 72 – 47.

Jason's thinking:

$72 - 47 = ?$

First subtract 40 from 72.

$72 - 40 = 32$

Then subtract 2 (which is part of the 7 of the 47).

$32 - 2 = 30$

Finally, subtract the remaining 5 from the 30.

$30 - 5 = 25$

Interestingly, Jason started on the left with the tens column. Then he apparently tried to make the number "friendlier," getting a zero in the ones column by breaking the remaining 7 (of the original 47) into 2 and 5. This step seems to eliminate the usual problems associated with borrowing. Going from $32 - 2 = 30$ and $30 - 5 = 25$ was easier than $32 - 7 = 25$.

Bert's thinking:

$72 - 47 = ?$

$72 - 10 = 62$

$62 - 10 = 52$

$52 - 10 = 42$

$42 - 10 = 32$

$32 - 7 = 25$

Bert used a process similar to the one he had used in addition, namely, breaking up the smaller number into friendlier pieces. Thus, he viewed the 47 as $10 + 10 + 10 + 10 + 7$. Then he subtracted 10 at a time. After arriving at the 32, he used the traditional borrowing procedure to solve the remaining part, $32 - 7$.

As Jason had done, Bert started on the left with the tens column and subtracted groups of 10. He did get bogged down when he had to take away the 7. This final step wasn't as automatic for him as the earlier steps.

Holly's idea for $72 - 47$ was similar to Bert's, except that it eliminated the need to regroup in the traditional way. She first took away 2 from

110

115

120

125

130

135

both 72 and 47, thus creating a new but equivalent problem: 70 – 45. She   140
then subtracted in units of 10 four times, and finally subtracted the 5.

Holly's thinking:

$72 – 47 = ?$

Take 2 away from both to make 70 – 45.

$70 – 10 = 60$ 145

$60 – 10 = 50$

$50 – 10 = 40$

$40 – 10 = 30$

$30 – 5 = 25$

This ability to create a new problem with an equivalent answer by   150
subtracting the same amount from both numbers was thought-provoking
for some of my students. Kristy stated, "We could add the same amount
to each number and also get the same answer."

Sam pointed out how this equivalency was the same as in fractions.
He said, "When you multiply the parts of fractions, you come up with   155
equivalent fractions: $\frac{1}{2} = \frac{3}{6}$." This sense of equivalency intrigues me
because it seems to connect with ideas across topic areas such as whole
numbers and fractions.

Other problems prompted some new ideas from the class. Joe's
thinking for the problem 82 – 35 was first to subtract 2 from 82 and 5   160
from 35 so he could look at 80 – 30 = 50. Then he subtracted 5 from 2 and
got 3. (He never questioned taking the bigger number from the smaller
number, and he did not say he meant –3.) Finally he subtracted 3 from 50
and got 47.

This strategy fascinated both the class and me. It seemed to touch   165
upon negative numbers. We tried it on many other problems, such as this
one:

$63 – 25 = ?$

$63 – 3 = 60$ and $25 – 5 = 20$

$60 – 20 = 40$ 170

$3 – 5 = 2$

$40 – 2 = 38$

Together we also tried it on a problem that didn't need regrouping:

$54 - 22 = ?$

$54 - 4 = 50$ and $22 - 2 = 20$

$50 - 20 = 30$

$4 - 2 = 2 \ldots$

At this point, some students realized that we needed to add the 2 to the 30 instead of subtracting it, because there was no regrouping involved:

$30 + 2 = 32$

For the same problem that Joe talked about, $82 - 35$, Jennifer stated that she looked at "subtraction as addition."

$$\begin{array}{r} 82 \\ -\ 35 \\ \hline \end{array}$$

First, Jennifer felt she would have to "borrow" from the tens column so she could take away 5 from the 2. She thought, "5 + ? = 12." Then she thought, "30 + ? = 70." She plugged in the 7 and the 40, respectively, for the answer of 47. Seeing a reversible relationship between subtraction and addition, Jennifer used this understanding to help solve computational problems.

Kristy and Chad shared the following thinking for the problem $75 - 27$:

First we switched the numbers in the ones column so that $7 - 5 = 2$. We saved this 2 for later.

Then we subtracted:

$70 - 20 = 50$

Finally, we subtracted the 2 we had saved:

$50 - 2 = 48$

This was interesting to watch because it generated a great deal of "what if" situations from my students, such as "What if there wasn't regrouping [as in $77 - 25$]?" They decided that "when the number is bigger" you don't switch, and you *add* the answer to the final number instead of subtracting it.

$77 - 25 = ?$

$7 - 5 = 2$

$70 - 20 = 50$

$50 + 2 = 52$

205

They also posed the question, "What if it were a three-digit number? Would it still work?" We tried it on the problem $438 - 279$.

$9 - 8 = 1$

$70 - 30 = 40$

210

$400 - 200 = 200$

$200 - 40 = 160$

$160 - 1 = 159$

It worked!

I saw a connection with Joe's subtraction thinking, but no one else noticed or pointed it out.

215

The belief that the traditional algorithm is how elementary students (or even adults) "see" subtraction is far from true. Students construct their own ideas of what subtraction is and how to represent it. As teachers, we must realize that when we tell or show students how to do any mathematical process, that process is interpreted in as many different ways as there are students. When all our students can tell us that $57 - 18 = 39$, we must not be fooled into thinking that they all know the exact same things. Only by giving each student a voice in math instruction, and *listening* to it, can we truly see the depth of their understandings.

220

225

Children inventing their own addition procedures

Sandra

GRADE 2, MAY

My second graders have been working on addition of two-digit numbers. They are already used to naming numbers in different ways; we often take the date, or the number of days we have been in school, and make a game of renaming that number. So, for example, 27 might be 25 + 2, or 30 – 3. I was interested to see how they would apply their renaming skills to solve problems in which the sum of the digits in the ones column is greater than 10.

I presented the following problem to the class and made sure that everyone could read it:

> **?** Kira had 48 cents in her pocket. Her big brother gave her 25 cents for running an errand. Now how much does she have?

I gave the children each a sheet of paper with the problem and asked them to solve it, individually first, in more than one way. Then they would share their strategies with a partner or with their group.

Coins, 100 number boards, and Multilink™ cubes were available to use if they wanted. Some children chose the 100 number board, and one used coins, but most of the children solved the problem using number sentences.

As soon as work was underway, I went over to Tomo, a Japanese child with limited English vocabulary, and asked him if he understood the problem. It was obvious that he didn't, so I read the problem again to him and explained it further with gestures and simple words until he understood it.

The children worked for about five minutes on their own and then began talking to each other. Twenty minutes after we got started, I called the group together to share their strategies. As each child went to the board to show the class what he or she had done, I took notes to record

230

235

240

245

250

the variety of ways they used renaming to perform the calculation
48 + 25.

LASHAY: I took the 8 from the 48 and the 5 from the 25. And I added: 255

        5 + 8 = 13

        40 + 20 = 60

        60 + 13 = 73

ABBY: First I wrote 48 and 25 and I put the 8 and the 5 in the save
        box. Then I did 40 + 20 = 60. Then I made the 5 into a 2 and   260
        put 3 in the save box.

        8 + 2 = 10

        60 + 10 = 70

        70 + 3 = 73

KEVIN: First I did 48 + 20 = 68. Then 68 + 2 (from the 5) = 70. Then I   265
        still had 3 from the 5, so 70 + 3 = 73.

WANDA: 40 plus 20 equals 60. Then I had 8 and 5. I split the 8 into
        two numbers (5 + 3).

        5 + 5 = 10

        60 + 10 = 70   270

        70 + 3 = 73

AKEEM: I had 20 and I had the 5 from the 25 because I splitted it in
        half. I had another 20 from the 48, so that left me 28.

        20 + 20 = 40

        28 + 5 = 33   275

        40 + 33 = 73

Ian explained that he started at 48 on the 100 number board and
counted by tens to 68. Then he got a little confused and thought it would
not work. I told him that he was on the right track, so he persevered. He
saw that he now needed to continue counting by ones, and counted from   280
68 to 73.

After class, I looked through the other children's papers and found
still more methods.

48×25

IMANI:	40 + 20 = 60	
	60 + 8 = 68	285
	68 + 5 = 73	
KIM:	25 + 40 = 65	
	65 + 8 = 73	
DEREK:	48 = 25 + 23	
	25 + 25 = 50	290
	50 + 23 = 73	
JAMEEL:	48 − 3 = 45	
	45 + 25 = 70	
	70 + 3 = 73	
DAVID:	40 + 20 = 60	295
	8 = 4 + 4	
	60 + 4 = 64	
	64 + 4 = 68	
	68 + 5 = 73?	

Almost all the children used renaming strategies to solve the problem, and almost all the renaming involved either breaking the numbers apart into their tens and ones components or combining numbers to form multiples of ten, or both. Some children broke up their numbers to create doubles.

A very few children simply counted by ones, such as Terry, who used the 100 number board to help her keep track. Jake, who decided to use coins, made pictures of the coins he was using to represent the amounts he needed.

As I look over the variety of solution methods, I am convinced of the value of children sharing their strategies within small groups and with the whole class. While the children are explaining their approaches to the problem, their thinking gets clarified. Additionally, all the children benefit from listening to other children's strategies. This becomes evident on days following these sessions, when children begin to use the strategies that others shared. I expect to see this soon with the strategies that were presented today.

300

305

310

315

Learning math while teaching

Emily

GRADE 2, MARCH

Recently I watched children solve two-digit subtraction problems. I was eager to observe their different ways of approaching a problem and getting an answer that made sense to them. I was prepared to see confusion and lots of different methods; I felt very open. However, I was surprised and delighted to learn a new way to solve a two-digit subtraction problem, one I had never thought of or even imagined before. I still have to picture it and think it through carefully as I retell it here.

Ivan was working with two or three other kids on the same word problem that led them each to this equation: $52 - 28 = ?$ At first, Ivan said the answer was 36, but Brandon had gotten 24, so now the two were talking with each other. Brandon saw clearly what Ivan had done and was explaining to him why it was wrong. Ivan believed him and agreed with what Brandon said: "20 away from 50 is 30, but you can't take the 2 away from the 8; you have to take the 8 away from the 2 because the 8 is on the bottom."

I imagined Ivan responding "but you can't take the 8 away from the 2 because the 8 is too big." I further imagined encouraging Brandon to explain more about what he had done, expecting they would talk through something about borrowing a 10 from the 50 to make the 2 into a 12. But as I watched, Ivan invented this new method:

"You take the 20 away from the 50 and get 30. Then you take 8 away from 2 which is –6. Then you take –6 away from 30 and you get 24."

I've since read Connie Kamii's book (1989) in which she describes several common methods that second graders use to subtract in this situation, and Ivan's method was one of them. It still feels new enough to me that I have to think it through each time. It is definitely a case of my learning some mathematics from my students.

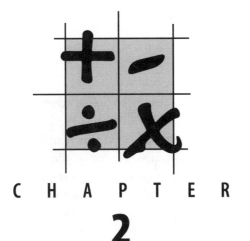

C H A P T E R

2

Recognizing and keeping track of groups of 10 while operating

CASE 5	Thinking about tens	*Janine, Grade 4, October*
CASE 6	Keeping it straight	*Lucy, Grade 3, November*
CASE 7	Beyond one hundred	*Beverly, Grade 1, May*
CASE 8	This is confusing, this 8 and 9 thing	*Emily, Grade 2, February*
CASE 9	Counting cubes	*Regina, Grade 3, October*
CASE 10	Counting money	*Kara, Grade 3, November*

In chapter 1, you read about methods that children invented to perform multidigit addition and subtraction. Although the cases describe particular children in just three classrooms, their methods are quite typical of the ways children think when they are encouraged to think things through for themselves. However, in order to invent these methods, the children must already understand a number of things. They certainly must have a clear idea of what it means to add and subtract (a subject explored more deeply in the DMI casebook

Making Meaning for Operations). But they must also understand various ways that numbers can be decomposed and recombined.

In the cases in chapter 2, the children are working hard to put together the ideas they need in order to use numbers flexibly. Many of the children are confused—that's what makes these good cases to study. That is, when children are doing everything correctly, the hard thinking they have done is often invisible. On the other hand, if we examine their thinking when they are confused, the ideas they are working on are often easier to identify. The students in cases 5–10 are working to figure out how components of numbers recombine during addition. As you read the following cases, take notes on these questions:

- In what ways does the children's thinking make sense?
- What are the ideas they are putting together?

In several cases, children are working with manipulative materials to represent number. If you have the manipulatives on hand, it would be a good idea to act out exactly what the children do with them. If the manipulatives are unfamiliar to you, spend some time yourself discovering how they can be used to represent number before you try to analyze the children's thinking.

C A S E 5

Thinking about tens

Janine

GRADE 4, OCTOBER

I have been working with my fourth-grade class on a variety of exercises aimed at evaluating the level of mathematical thinking and skills of the students. For the most part, the class seems pretty much where you would expect students to be at the beginning of fourth grade. They have strengths in certain areas and weaknesses in others (as do we all!). The particular lesson we have been working on recently, in *Mathematical*

5

Janine

Thinking at Grade 4 from the curriculum *Investigations in Number, Data, and Space*® (Dale Seymour Publications, 1998), involves what are called "cluster problems." These are groupings of computation problems that are somehow related to one another. Here is an example of a cluster problem:

$$5 + 3 = ?$$

$$15 + 3 = ?$$

$$25 + 3 = ?$$

$$35 + 13 = ?$$

$$85 + 23 = ?$$

Students are to solve mentally any of the problems that they can, and then use those answers to help them solve the other problems that are more difficult. For example, students are expected to notice that all the numbers in the ones place are either 5 or 3, and that the only thing changing is the number of tens that they need to add. Most of my students had little difficulty solving these problems and verbalizing the methods they used to solve them—all except Serena.

I happened to be standing next to Serena's desk while another student presented a strategy for solving cluster problems, and I noticed that Serena's worksheet was literally covered with little tally marks she was using to help her solve the addition problems. Now, these addition problems should not have been difficult for fourth graders, since the point of the lesson was not the addition itself, but rather seeing the relationships between numbers that have something in common. When I had a minute, I sat with Serena and asked her about her work. She said that she needed the little lines to help her add the numbers. OK—I saw we had a problem.

I pointed at one of the examples Serena was working on, 18 + 24, and asked her to explain how she was figuring out the number. Maybe the horizontal layout of the problem was causing the confusion. Could she have solved the problem if it had been written vertically? Serena explained that she made 18 lines and then 24 lines and counted them up. She had to do this several times because she kept losing count.

I asked if there might be an easier way to do this. She suggested she count them by twos, and did so. No problem there. How about an easier way? By threes? She proceeded to group the tally marks by threes, and then counted them by ones. No help there! Try again. This time she grouped them by fives and counted them up. My goal was to get her to tens, but that was not *her* goal!

I decided that Serena needed some help and needed it soon. I asked her if she would stay after school and work with me on her math, and she readily agreed.

Our first session took place the following afternoon. I decided to try the base ten blocks because I thought she had a real problem with visualizing numbers—and, boy, did she! She said she had used the blocks before, but you could have fooled me. We started with a simple addition problem:

> **?** There were 17 birds sitting in a tree, and 8 more joined them. How many birds were now in the tree?

As with her tally marks, Serena decided to use the unit cubes first, and again she had a really hard time keeping track of her counting. We talked about the ten-sticks as being equal to 10 of the units, matched them up, and tried the problem again. Every time Serena used the ten-stick, she had to count each and every unit to assure herself that there were really 10. When she finally got an answer of 25, she had to count all 25 by ones, even though she was using two ten-sticks. She didn't trust herself to say that a ten-stick was equal to 10, and that two of them made 20.

We did several more problems like this until Serena finally felt comfortable enough not to have to count out each of the tens, and this really took a while. We got up to problems like 43 + 56, and she was able to do this using tens and ones. I wanted her to see the relationship between the number (43, for example) and the fact that she had 4 ten-sticks and 3 unit-cubes. Each time she made a new number, I would ask her how many tens she used and how many ones, and point out the fact that this is what the number was actually telling her. She felt really pleased when she finally saw this relationship—that if you had the number 57, then you wound up with 5 ten-sticks and 7 units.

I'm sure that Serena is not the only one in my fourth-grade class who has difficulty making sense out of our number system, but at this time her problem seems the most severe. We're going to have to take it one step at a time and be really visual. Hopefully, down the road some, her next step will be to draw squares for hundreds, lines for tens, and small squares for ones. At least if she can do that, her calculations will be a little

more efficient than they are with hundreds of tally marks all over her
paper!

    Serena has made me realize, once again, just how much we take for
granted when working with our students. She seems to be a fairly bright
girl who just *never got it.*

80

C A S E   6

Keeping it straight

Lucy
GRADE 3, NOVEMBER

Over the past few weeks, as I give my third graders two-digit numbers to
add, I have been trying to understand what they think is happening with
the numbers. In each lesson, students first work in pairs, then share their
solutions with the whole class.

    At the end of a discussion last week, after the class had already looked
at several ways to show that 39 + 52 = 91, Sarah tried to explain yet
another way she had found. She understood all the various methods that
had been presented. In fact, Sarah is generally very fluent in thinking
about how numbers work. This time, when working with her partner, she
had tried hard to find an unusual way, hoping she would get to share it
during the discussion.

    Sarah showed us a stack of 3 cubes and explained that they equaled 30
because she was using one cube to show a ten. She held up a separate
stack of 9 and said that, together, the two stacks of cubes represented 39.
Then she pointed to a stack of 5 cubes, saying that it was 50 and, with
another stack of 2, showed 52. She took the 3-cube and 5-cube stacks and
added them together, saying it equaled 80. Then she put the 9-cube and 2-
cube "ones" stacks together, saying that they made 11. She then broke off
10 of the 11 cubes, attached them to the 8 cubes representing 80—and
looked up confused. She knew that the answer was 91, but her

85

90

95

100

arrangement of cubes didn't look like 91. Class was over, however. It was time for lunch.

I wondered how Sarah was connecting her work on this problem with what she thought she understood about adding. She had demonstrated in earlier lessons that she was already able to use the conventional algorithm to solve this type of problem. When given a similar problem to solve on paper, she had explained that she needed to "carry the 1" because there were too many ones. I wondered what she was thinking when she kept "carrying" the 10 individual cubes.

At the start of math the next day, the class reviewed all the methods they had shared for solving 39 + 52. I asked them to use each method to solve that day's problem, 45 + 39, and then we would discuss what they found.

After the class had been working for a while, I came to Sarah and her partner. They complained that three times they had done it "Sarah's way," and each time the answer was 174. It didn't make sense—they had already reached an answer of 84 doing it other ways. I knew it had really bothered Sarah the day before when the cubes hadn't shown her idea of the right answer. I was pleased with her persistence and joined the pair for a while.

They had built the numbers with Unifix® cubes, using yellow cubes for tens and black for ones. Thus they had 4 yellow and 5 black cubes representing 45, and 3 yellow and 9 black for 39.

TEACHER: What happens when you add the two numbers together?

SARAH: First I add the ones together. [*She puts all the black cubes into a stack.*] There are way too many to keep on the ones side, so I try to carry them.

I wanted Sarah to explain what she meant by this.

TEACHER: What do you mean, "there are way too many ones to have on the ones side" and you try to carry them? What does that mean?

SARAH: There are 14 ones and I'm doing this like a problem, so I have it, like, I'm sort of writing it, but using cubes instead of writing it.

Sarah pointed to the cubes; she had the tens arranged in a column and the ones in another column, vertically, one number below the other.

SARAH: There are too many ones to equal on this side. [*She points to the ones side.*]

TEACHER: OK.

SARAH: I carry the 1, so I take 10 away. [*She breaks off 10 of the black cubes.*]   145

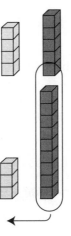

TEACHER: What do you mean, you take 10 away? Is that like subtracting?

SARAH: The answer is 14, so I'm trying to carry the 1. [*She is being very patient with all my questions.*]

TEACHER: And what is that 1 that you are trying to carry?   150

SARAH: The 1 is . . . tens.

TEACHER: OK.

SARAH: Each ten is 10 ones.

TEACHER: OK.

SARAH: So I take away 10 ones. [*She attaches them to the 7 yellow cubes and looks at what she has, a stack of 4 black cubes and a second stack of 17 yellow and black.*]   155

TEACHER: So you said your answer was 174.

SARAH: And so, here's my tens [*pointing to the yellow and black stack*] and here's my ones. [*Setting aside the 4 black cubes, she begins counting the yellow and black "tens."*] And it's 174.
160

TEACHER: And this is what you got before. [*Sarah's partner begins counting to make sure.*]

SARAH: [*Pondering*] I'm getting it. [*She has a brightness in her eyes like a light bulb coming on.*]
165

TEACHER: What do you think?

SARAH: If I put 10 of these up here [*pointing to the 10 black cubes attached above the yellow*] it equals 1, not just 10.

TEACHER: If you put 10 of what up there? [*I want her to be clearer about what she is saying.*]
170

SARAH: It equals 10 ones. It's 10. Not 100.

TEACHER: I'm not sure I know what you mean.

SARAH: When I took this [10 black cubes] from down here [*pointing back to the 4*], it is a ten.

TEACHER: It is a ten?
175

SARAH: It is *a* ten.

TEACHER: These 10 black Unifix cubes are a ten? [*Sarah picks up an extra yellow cube and attaches it to the other 7 yellow cubes.*] So you're saying this ten [stack of 10 blacks] is the same as this 1 yellow cube?
180

SARAH: [*Nodding and smiling*] It's 84. I know what I was doing wrong now.

TEACHER: I'm not sure you were doing anything wrong. You were just thinking of this 10 . . .

SARAH: As being 100.
185

TEACHER: Does your answer of 84 have anything to do with the work you did on your paper when you added the numbers the other ways? What does what you wrote on your paper have to do with what you just found out about that 10?

SARAH:	It's the same thing.	190
TEACHER:	What was it that you did the same?	
SARAH:	Like here. [*She picks up the paper on which she applied the traditional algorithm and points to the small 1 she had put above the 4.*] This 1 that I carried is not 10 ones, it's a ten. In the 14, there's a ten right here [*pointing to the digit 1 on her paper*].	195
TEACHER:	All right! Are you happy now? [*Sarah smiles.*] That was really bothering you, wasn't it?	

Now that I'm writing up this episode, I wish I had thought to ask Sarah what made her realize that the 10 cubes equaled a ten and needed to be represented with a single yellow cube. But I didn't. Maybe next time. ⎸200

It seems to me that Sarah's struggle with representing her work this way helps her make the connection to what's happening on paper when digits are moved around. I'll watch her work in coming days to see if I'm right. Now I have to find that connection for the other 16 kids! What ⎸205 Sarah was trying to show seemed important to me. It was interesting to have that dialogue with her—to go through her thinking with her, watching her ideas become clearer as she talked through her thinking. She was hooked. She knew there was something missing, something wrong, and it was important to her to find it and understand it. ⎸210

C A S E 7

Beyond one hundred

Beverly
GRADE 1, MAY

I have come to realize how much I myself can learn if I listen to children ⎸211 as they talk about mathematics. I'm on leave from teaching, so for my case study I decided to set up a series of sessions with Kim, a first grader who lives next door. Kim is a pretty typical kid. She's not a star in her school math class, nor is she behind. She seems delighted to meet with me. I think mainly she likes the adult attention. Recently we tried addition with and without regrouping.

The first problem I gave Kim was 27 + 12. I wrote the problem two different ways because I was not sure which way Kim preferred:

$$27 + 12 = \qquad \begin{array}{r} 27 \\ + 12 \\ \hline \end{array}$$

After I wrote the numbers down, I asked Kim if she could show me how she would figure out the answer. Kim stated confidently, "2 tens and 1 ten are 30. Then 27 and 1 ten is 37, and you add 2 more to get 39." Then she wrote the problem on paper:

$$\begin{array}{r} 27 \\ + 12 \\ \hline 39 \end{array}$$

I asked Kim, "What happened to the 2 tens and 1 ten are 30?" Kim said she was going to do it that way at first, but then she saw that 27 and 1 ten were 37.

I decided to give her some problems with bigger numbers to see what she could do with them. I verbally stated the next problem as I wrote it both ways, then asked Kim to show me how she would do it.

$$15 + 63 = \qquad \begin{array}{r} 15 \\ + 63 \\ \hline \end{array}$$

Kim immediately told me, "6 tens and 1 ten is 70 and 5 plus 3 equals 8, so 78."

The next problem I gave her involved regrouping. Again, I wrote it both horizontally and vertically and asked Kim to show me her thinking.

$$18 + 34 = \qquad \begin{array}{r} 18 \\ + 34 \\ \hline \end{array}$$

"I think it's going to be more than 50," she stated.

"How could you tell so fast?" I asked.

Kim answered, "I could tell that 1 ten and 3 tens was 40, so the answer would be about 50 because of the other numbers." Kim then did the computation on paper using the vertical form. She looked at her paper and stated, "3 tens and 1 ten is 40; 8 plus 4 equals 11 . . . no, 12. Then the answer is 52."

Because Kim seemed confident with the previous problems, I decided to give her one that was a bit more challenging. I wrote 79 + 56 in both formats, stating the problem verbally as I wrote. Kim said right away, "7 tens and 5 tens are 12 tens." I asked Kim if she could show me how to write that number. She answered, "I don't know. 102?"

Wanting to find out what Kim understood and where her confusions lay, I then asked if she knew how many tens are in 100. Her very confident response was "Ten." I thought it would be helpful for Kim to see the numbers written down as well as spoken. As I began to ask how many tens were in 110, we started to create a list:

100 = 10 tens

Kim wrote 110 and said there were 11 tens, adding that to our list. "How many tens are in 120?" I asked.

Kim hesitated and did not seem as sure as she had been. She wrote 120 on our list, and after waiting a little, I wrote 12 tens next to it. She didn't need further prompting. We continued in this way up to 150 = 15 tens, where Kim stopped writing but continued saying the numbers out loud up to "200 has 20 tens."

I then reminded her that she had previously stated 5 tens and 7 tens was 12 tens. I asked if she could find that number on our list. When she pointed to 120 = 12 tens, I circled it on the paper. She then continued with the original problem, 79 + 56. "6 ones and 9 ones is 15 ones. Then you take the ten from 15 ones and put it with 120 and get 130. Add the 5 ones and you have 135."

I continued to have questions about what Kim understood. This was the first time I ever saw her have difficulty recording her mathematical thinking. I gave her another problem that would challenge her under-standing of groups of 10: "How many fingers would all the kids in your class at school have?"

Kim answered that there were 21 children in the class and added, "You have to count ten 21 times, so 201." I suggested we do the thinking on paper. "We're going to count ten 21 times," I reminded her. Kim wrote the numbers as she said them out loud.

Beverly

```
10  20  30 40
   50 60 70
  80  90 100
 110 120 130
140 150 160
170 180
190 200
210
```

Her paper shows that she wrote 180 instead of 170 initially, but she corrected this without prompting. For 210 she started to write 201, then changed the 0 in the tens place to a 1 and wrote 210.

I wonder how solid her understanding of place value for numbers over a hundred really is, since she needed me to provide a meaningful context for her, as well as some support. Is her problem conceptual, or is it just a matter of notation? What kind of problems can I pose to find out?

C A S E   8

This is confusing, this 8 and 9 thing

Emily

I am generally intrigued by the notion of regrouping and what kids in second grade know about what happens when there is more than 10 in the ones column. In first grade in my school, the children have all been taught to use Cuisenaire® rods to solve mathematical problems. They know how to use the rods to perform all four operations. Cuisenaire rods

280

285

are similar to base ten blocks, except that each number (1 through 10) is represented by a solid rod that cannot be taken apart into discrete units.

The child who is the focus of this case is Julie. I noticed her confusion while meeting with a small group of eight students. The children were all working on the same word problem and had a huge pile of Cuisenaire rods on the rug in front of them. The word problem was this:

? Sam and Alyssa were walking on the beach at low tide. As they walked, they collected beach glass, which they put in their pockets. When they got home, they counted their glass. Sam had 38 pieces and Alyssa had 59 pieces. How many pieces of beach glass did they have?

The kids who solved this problem successfully manipulated the rods in a few different ways. They started out the same way, taking 5 tens and a 9-rod and 3 tens and an 8-rod.

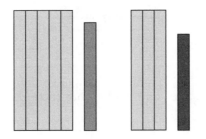

Then they added 50 and 30 and got 80.

From this point, the methods diverged somewhat. The kids using one method added 9 to the 80 to make 89, and then added 8 more by counting on their fingers: 90, 91, 92, 93, 94, 95, 96, 97.

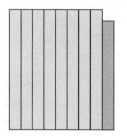

Those using a second method added 8 and 9, and found that it is the same as 10 and 7, so they replaced the 8-rod and 9-rod with a 10-rod and a 7-rod. They placed the "new" 10 with the 80, and added the 7 to get 97.   310

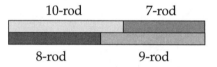

Julie started out similarly. She combined all her rods like this:

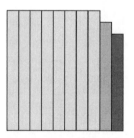

Julie explained to me that there were 8 tens when it is 80. Then there are this 8 and 9, "but they're too big." She moved the 8 and 9 around. She kept counting up the tens and got 80 each time, but the 8 and the 9 remained a problem to her. She sighed and said, "So I took the 8 away.   315
Then I have 89."
    I said, "But what about the 8?"

She shrugged and picked it up again and said (not sounding very convinced), "Yeah. OK. It's 88." We went back and forth once or twice more; she would take one of the rods away, and I would ask, "But what about the other?"

I said, "Gee, this is confusing, this 8 and 9 thing." Julie simply looked at me and raised her eyebrows.

During our conversation, my understanding grew clearer about her original statement that 8 and 9 are "too big." I am quite sure she was recognizing that in fact there is no 17-rod, no solid rod that would measure both 8 and 9 together. I'm also sure that something very perplexing was going on in her brain, but I'm not sure what or why or how.

Julie was sighing a lot, and it had been a long session, so I said, "Do you want to just leave this alone and know that you've done some hard thinking, or do you want me to help you figure it out?"

"Figure it out."

I began by asking, "What is 8 + 9?"

Julie shrugged and said, "I don't know."

I said, "Really? You really don't know what 8 and 9 are?"

"Nope."

This really surprised me, as I've seen her do this kind of single-digit addition problem many times.

I picked up the 8 and the 9, put them end to end, and said, "You could solve it by starting like this. Or you could add on your fingers," and I flicked my fingers.

Julie said, "Oh, yeah." She laid the 8 and 9 end to end and measured them with a 10-rod and a 7-rod. "It's 17, " she said.

10-rod   7-rod

8-rod   9-rod

So I touched the 8 tens that she had already, and then the 10 and the 7, and asked, "So now can you add these all up?"

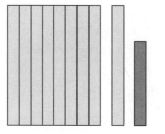

She counted by tens to 90 and knew that 7 more was 97. She then went off to snack period with the rest of the class.

Now I'm left wondering what this means. I wonder if, in the transformation of the 8 and 9 to a 10 and a 7, she holds onto the idea that 8 and 9 is equivalent to 10 and 7. Does the problem stop being 38 + 59 when the 8 and 9 stop being 8 and 9? Would she have made more sense of the 8 and 9 if they had been made up of discrete ones, rather than the solid 8 and solid 9? Did she have any connection to the original problem?

350

C A S E 9

Counting cubes

Regina
GRADE 3, OCTOBER

As I began my second year of teaching the third grade, one of my first priorities was to assess what my students already knew about mathematics. How much number sense were they bringing with them into third grade? How much facility did they exhibit in taking numbers apart and putting them back together? Could they talk about ones, tens, and hundreds, and if so, did they truly understand what they meant by these terms? Had learning the conventional addition and subtraction algorithms in the second grade in any way inhibited their ability to work creatively with numbers? Were they able to communicate their mathematical ideas both orally and in writing? All of these questions seemed

355

360

key both in assessing their prior knowledge and in determining how best to proceed with my mathematics instruction.

Unfortunately, my assessment was interrupted when, during what would have been our first full week of classes, our building was flooded by a massive water-main break, necessitating the closing of the school. Five days later, after moving more than 1,000 students and all of our books, furnishings, and supplies, we resumed classes in what had been a vacant building. Needless to say, it was like starting the year all over again, only under much more trying conditions. While moving over the weekend into the new building, I realized that I wasn't even sure whether I remembered the names of all of my students, never mind how much they knew about mathematics. So much for all of my best intentions about getting the year off to a good start.

It wasn't until October that things began to settle down a bit. Since finally getting underway, a number of episodes during our math class have particularly interested me. Although these episodes have helped me assess my students mathematically, they also raise further questions about how children move from one level of understanding to another. The following episode occurred when my students were working in pairs on counting out and proving that they had 100 interlocking cubes.

Although most pairs approached this task by counting by ones, twos, fives, or tens, Melissa and Carmen quickly devised another approach. The two girls first decided to sort their blocks by color. (Since I had given each group a random assortment of blocks, the number of blocks of each color was different.) After completing this sorting activity, which they did by counting each color by ones, both girls listed the results in their journals in the form of a two-column table, with one column labeled "colors" and the other labeled "cubes" (see Figure 1). Then the question arose, What could they do with this information? How could they best proceed from the number of blocks of each color to find out whether or not they had a total of 100 blocks?

At this point I noticed that the girls had stopped working together. Carmen was working intently by herself while Melissa appeared a little lost. I decided to investigate.

TEACHER: I see that you wrote down the number of blocks of each color. That's an interesting idea. Do you know how you are going to use that information to find out whether or not you have 100 blocks?

CARMEN: I'm adding together all the numbers to see how many we have.

Melissa seemed overwhelmed by the idea of doing that much adding. When I asked her how she thought they could figure out how many cubes they had, she looked confused.

TEACHER: Can you think of any other way to arrange the blocks to help you figure out how many there are?

MELISSA: I'm going to count them again to make sure that I have the right numbers.

Melissa seemed determined to recount the blocks, which she proceeded to do, again by ones. I decided to focus my attention once more on Carmen. I noticed that Carmen had added a third column of numbers between the original two columns in her table. This column appeared to be a running total. I was interested in finding out how Carmen had arrived at these numbers. I knew from some previous work we had done that Carmen was very fond of the conventional addition algorithm. She claimed that it was the addition strategy she always used and that she had no trouble "carrying" numbers in her head and keeping it all straight. Had she used this or a different strategy to come up with the running total?

TEACHER: You've done some interesting work here. What strategy did you use to come up with these numbers?

CARMEN: I just kept adding them up. I added 23 and 17 and got 40. Then I added 3 more and got 43, and 3 more and got 46, and I just kept going until I got to 94. That's how many blocks there are.

TEACHER: I see. How did you know that $23 + 17 = 40$?

CARMEN: I added 3 plus 7 and got 10. I put down the 0 and carried the 1. I added 2 plus 1 and got 3 and 1 more is 4. That's 40.

When I asked Carmen if she could tell me what the various digits represented, she was able to tell me which were tens and which were ones. I still was not convinced that she really understood what all of this

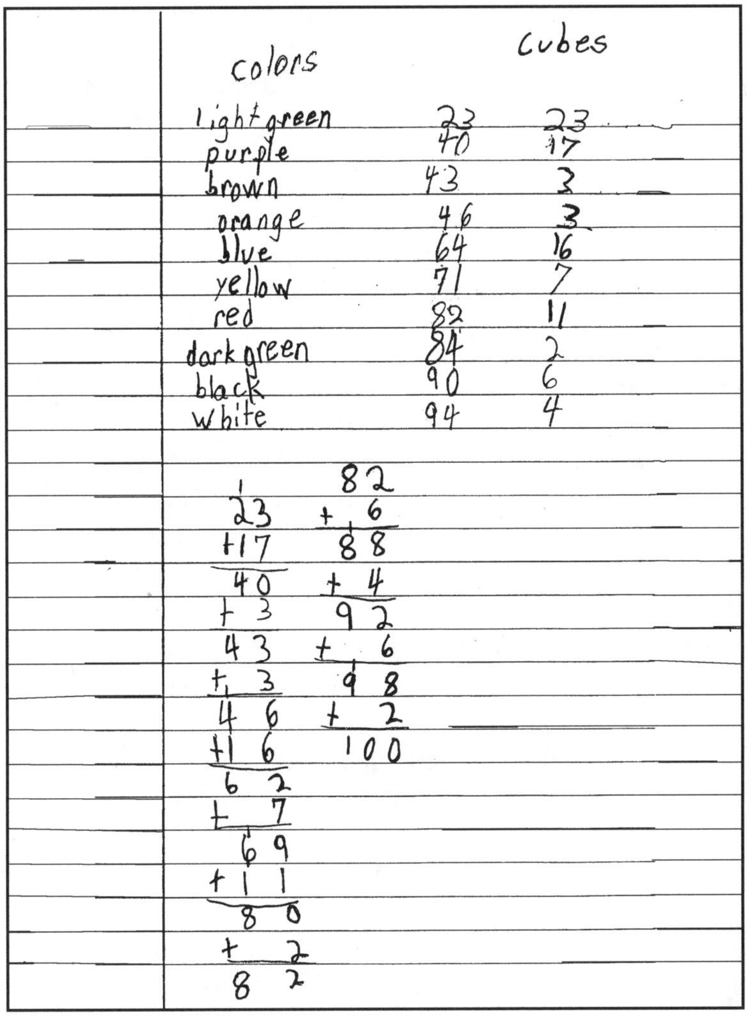

Figure 1 Carmen, a third grader, works on determining if she and her partner have 100 blocks.

meant. I had also noticed an addition mistake in her running total. I thought this was an opportunity to see if Carmen might try another approach.

TEACHER: You did a really good job of adding these numbers, Carmen. I did notice that you seem to be a little off on your count. Can you think of a way to check your answer?

Carmen then began to write out the addition sequence in pairs, still using the conventional algorithm (see bottom half of Figure 1). Melissa, in the meantime, had finished recounting the individual colors. Upon seeing Carmen's first total of 94 blocks, Melissa had gone to get 6 more. Carmen added these 6 to her new total of 92, realized that she needed 2 more, and added those to get a total of 100. Both girls seemed satisfied with their efforts.

TEACHER: That's great. How can you check your answer? Can you think of any way you can arrange these blocks now so that you can quickly prove to me and your classmates that you have 100 blocks?

I thought at this point that the girls might arrange their blocks in sticks of tens, or perhaps fives, to quickly check their total. I was surprised when they put them all together in one long line and began counting by ones. Both Melissa and Carmen seemed equally comfortable with this approach. When I questioned whether there might not be a quicker or easier way, they seemed completely unfazed and continued to count by ones. (In other words, I think they wanted me to get lost!)

What greatly interested me was the fact that both girls seemed so comfortable with counting the blocks out by ones, and yet they exhibited such different levels of mathematical understanding. Melissa was overwhelmed by all the numbers they had generated, while Carmen approached the task of adding up all those numbers with great enthusiasm. Yet it didn't occur to either girl that making groups of ten would be a quick and efficient way to solve this problem, which leaves me with a number of questions. Did Carmen really see the tens and ones in all her numbers? Did her pride in mastery of the conventional algorithm hold her back from trying other approaches that may have been more direct? Also, Melissa was clearly impressed by how "good" Carmen is in math. Had she been working alone or with another partner, would she have approached this problem in a completely different way?

There is an interesting postscript to this episode. When I told the students that it was time to clean up, I asked them to put their cubes in sticks of ten. Melissa was amazed and excited to realize that their blocks made 10 groups of ten, and she called me over to comment on this discovery. Carmen didn't say anything.

Counting money

Kara

Upon visiting my colleague's class this morning, I watch the children counting coins to solve the following:

? Nicholas has one dollar, two quarters, five dimes, five nickels, and thirteen pennies. How much money does he have? $2.38   480

I decide to spend some time with Tania to see how far her understanding has come since my previous visit a week ago.

As I approach Tania, I am somewhat surprised and excited to see her already working. Previously, I've observed that she takes a long time to get started. Tania has a pile of plastic coins in front of her, and she seems to be moving them and counting. She now knows that I like to hear her thinking, so when I sit down next to her, Tania returns to the beginning of the pile and says, as she pulls out two half-dollars, "This is one dollar." Then she slides two quarters into the new pile and says, "A dollar fifty." She stops, picks up her pencil, and writes $1.00, then crosses it out with a slash and writes 50 below it. (See her work in Figure 2, on the part of the page labeled "Frist way.")   490

Slowly, and with great concentration, Tania begins to add in the nickels, counting "55, 60, 65, 70, 75" as she moves each nickel from one pile to the next. She returns to her recording page, crosses out the 50, and writes 75. She continues with the dimes, but gets confused when she reaches 100: "85, 95, 100, that's two dollars." Unable to cross the 100 barrier, she has difficulty adding 10 to 95 and comes up with 100. Perhaps she feels that most counting ends with 100, and this should too? Tania turns to her paper, puts a slash through the 75, and writes $2.00. She adds the remaining dimes, saying "2 dollars and 10 cents, 2 dollars and 20 cents." Then she adds on the pennies, "21, 22, . . ., 33."   495   500

Tania sits back in her chair, looks satisfied, and says, "Now I have to think of a different way." Although she is ready to move on, I am still   505 interested in discussing her first method. I also think that reflecting on this one might help her find another solving technique that will also make sense to her.

TEACHER: Why did you decide to do it this way?

TANIA: [*Shrugging*] I don't know.   510

TEACHER: You seemed to have a plan before you solved the problem. What was it?

TANIA: I wanted to do it the same way as the problem. [*She shows me the written problem.*] From highest to lowest.

The way the problem is written, it presents the coins from greater value   515
to lesser value. Tania chose to take the information as it was presented, but she also realized that it was organized. That organization system made enough sense to her to use it to solve the problem.

After a few minutes of quiet thinking, Tania begins writing column labels on her paper: "doller, dimes, nickels, quarters, penny." (See Tania's   520
"second way" at the bottom of Figure 2.) She turns to me and says, "I'm gonna make 100 little lines for a dollar, and 5, 10, 15—no, 10, 20, 30, 40, 50, for the dimes." Here Tania has self-corrected, realizing that at first she was counting the dimes by fives rather than by tens. She shows confidence in her willingness to calmly yet quickly clarify her thoughts.   525

I've seen many children use the "little lines" method of counting; they usually find that it is unsuccessful because of a lack of organization. Most children draw lines and count them, lose count, and begin again, often several times. So I decide to try to help Tania with another strategy.

TEACHER: When I try to use lines to keep track of something, I usually   530
lose count and have to start again. I think it can be very confusing. If you are going to draw 100 lines, could you just write the number 100 instead?

TANIA: [*Thinks about this suggestion and looks unsure.*] Yeah.

She begins writing amounts under the titles. As in her first method,   535
each time she records the next amount, she crosses out the previous one. She hesitates when she comes to the quarters, but then says, "2 dollars, 2 dollars and 25 cents." Next she counts the pennies and gets a total of 38

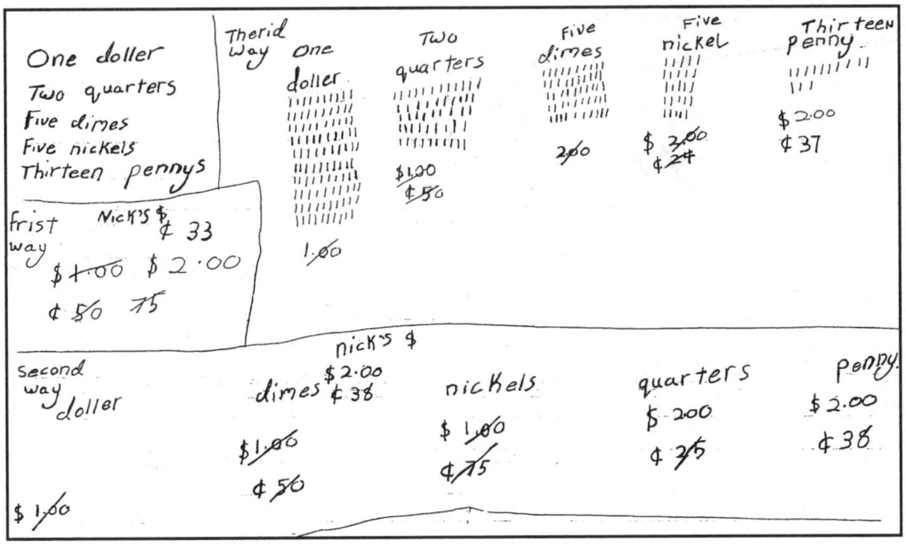

Figure 2 Third-grader Tania finds more than one way to total 1 dollar, 2 quarters, 5 dimes, 5 nickels, and 13 pennies.

cents. She records this, and speaks, her forehead wrinkled: "That's a different answer." Indeed, she got $2.33 using her first method and $2.38 using the second.

TEACHER: Which answer do you feel more confident about?

TANIA: This one [*indicating $2.38*].

TEACHER: Why?

TANIA: I don't know. I just think this is the real answer.

The class is called together for a group discussion, and Tania moves toward the group. I sit down, feeling quite satisfied by the work Tania has done.

Several days later, the classroom teacher gives me a copy of Tania's recording sheet for this problem. Tania had added what she labels a "Therid way" of solving the problem during the next day's work. She had drawn little lines under each coin name, doing what she'd wanted to do when we worked together. I thought she had understood the connection I had suggested between the lines and the numbers. But

540

545

550

apparently she still needed to draw all the lines. What role do the tally marks play for a child in this kind of counting? Does Tania draw the lines because of a need to see the physical amount of each number? Was there any value in my suggesting that Tania circumvent the "little lines" method, or should I have quietly allowed her to follow through on her own idea? Once again, I am forced to reflect on my role as a teacher.

555

560

Written numerals and
the structure of tens and ones

I n chapter 3, we continue the investigation of children's understandings of
how numbers are decomposed, but take another step back for a wider
perspective. Rather than examine children who are working on computation,
we consider children who are learning about how the components of a number
relate to written numerals. It is easy for adults to see, for example, that the
numeral 706 represents 7 hundreds, 0 tens, and 6 ones. However, when we
study children who are in the process of learning, we discover that this idea is
not so simple.

As you read chapter 3, take notes on these issues:

- In the following cases, some of the children offer incorrect answers. Look for elements of logic in their thinking. If the children are working from a logical position, where does their thinking go awry?

- In other cases, the children are talking about their own new insights. What are these insights and how do they come about?

Although the cases present the thinking of children in primary grades, teachers of older children can gain insight into their students' thinking as well. In subsequent chapters, we will see children sorting out these same ideas in the contexts of multiplying and dividing multidigit numbers and learning to work with decimals.

C A S E 11

Number of days in school

Dawn

KINDERGARTEN, DECEMBER

Each morning, as my kindergarten class gathers on the meeting rug, we run through a routine that helps set our day in motion. This set of rituals includes taking attendance, working with our classroom calendar and weather graph, and recording how many days we have been in school. It is amazing how much mathematics is involved in these activities, and often I am astounded by the thoughtful responses five- and six-year-olds give to such questions as, "What number should we record on our days-in-school chart today?" This morning, our sixtieth day of school, we turned to our days-in-school chart.

Over the years, I have spent a lot of time thinking about the optimal way to record this data with kindergarten students. Many years ago I used a number line that spanned the top of the chalkboard, but found that this was too physically removed from the children, not to mention extremely cumbersome for me. Having seen in the past the merits of

5

10

using hundreds boards when working with older students, I wondered if
this type of grid might have a place in the kindergarten classroom as
well. About ten years ago I made a switch to this type of recording
system for tracking how many days we have been in school each year.
Every day I record the number on our 10-by-18 grid, and the child who is
the calendar-helper adds one seashell to a cup that we keep nearby. This
provides a set of concrete objects that corresponds to the number being
logged on the chart. From time to time, the children count this set of
shells, and we then compare our two types of recording systems to
connect the quantity of shells with the number we count, read, and write.
If necessary, we then adjust our data.

1	2	3	4	5	6	7	8	9	10
11	12	13	14	15	16	17	18	19	20
21	22	23	24	25	26	27	28	29	30
31	32	33	34	35	36	37	38	39	40
41	42	43	44	45	46	47	48	49	50
51	52	53	54	55	56	57	58	59	

To begin our discussion this morning, I asked, "What number should I
write on our chart today?" Hands shot up and I began writing responses
on the chalkboard next to our chart, hoping to allow as many children as
possible to respond before recording the "right answer" on the grid.
Often this type of discussion yields some interesting discoveries. Today
was no exception.

ANDREW: I think it's 5 and 10. [*I wrote 510 on the board.*]

JOSEF: Sixty. [*I wrote 60.*]

More hands shot up, and Bianca, Jared, Rhea, Terry, Toshi, Pat, John, Sione, Susan, and Brady all responded "Sixty." Some children added other comments, too.

TOSHI: I know it's 60. I just know it is.

Jared, John, and Sione were equally emphatic. Susan seemed a little less sure, but apparently wanted to go along with the general consensus. Still more responses kept coming as more hands were up.

TAMIKA: Forty. [*I wrote 40.*]

JERREL: Eight. [*I wrote 8.*]

NINA: Seventy. [*I wrote 70.*]

"How can we find out which number we should write today?" I asked, to continue our discussion.

BIANCA: Counting, so we could know what comes next.

JOSEF: All the numbers are in front of it, 'cause 6 comes after 5, you know.

As Josef spoke, he moved up to the chart and pointed to the column of numbers on the right hand side, stopping at the empty box under the 50.

JARED: Yeah, see, zero all the way down.

ANDREW: Don't forget the 10.

Once again, physical involvement seemed a necessity as Andrew moved up to the chart and dragged his finger across the row with the numbers 51, 52, 53, 54, 55, 56, 57, 58, and 59. Andrew seemed to be making use of the number (counting) sequence; thus his response of a 5 and a 10 (510) made perfect sense.

BRADY: But it's a 6. [*Again, moving up to point at the chart, Brady's finger slid down the right hand column just as Toshi's and Jared's had as they spoke.*] See, 1, 2, 3, 4, 5, and 6 goes here 'cause you're counting down.

TOSHI: See, it's 60. I know it is.

Sitting toward the back of the group was Norman. Though he didn't speak out in front of the group, my aide was taking notes and later related to me that he was making comments under his breath.

NORMAN: It can't be 8. We already had that one. . . . Five and ten looks like five hundred and ten. That is too big to go there.

Because we needed to move on, I ended this discussion by reminding the children that another way to check was to use Bianca's suggested strategy of counting. Together, as I pointed to each number on our chart, we counted from 1 to 60 and agreed that 60 was the number to be written in the box for today. As we finished, there were two final comments:

JOSEF: Are we going to get 100?

BRADY: Yes, 'cause look, we can count by tens: 10, 20, 30, 40, 50, 60. I think we will get to more than 100.

As I reflect on these events, I am particularly taken by the ease with which some children are able to connect to the systematic way we use numbers. At the same time, I know for sure that not all children in my class are making sense of this experience at this time. Trying to provide opportunities where young children can investigate numbers in a meaningful way is a challenge.

C A S E   12

Groups and leftovers

Donna

GRADE 2, MARCH

At the beginning of March, I was trying to decide how to introduce place value. My goal was to help the children develop an understanding of how our number system works so that they would have a solid foundation when we began to work on adding and subtracting that involved regrouping. I decided there were two paths I could follow: I could set up some activities that would guide the children to make certain observations and connections, or I could start with word problems and work from there. Unfortunately, I didn't feel completely comfortable with either route. The activities that guided the children toward a particular end seemed too planned and constrained, and I wasn't comfortable spending a lot of time on these. On the other hand, I felt there were really important concepts about place value that might not surface if I didn't set up the situation for it to happen. So I decided to compromise. We would set the stage with one activity that focused on grouping tens and proceed from there.

I adapted an activity I had seen in Van de Walle's *Elementary School Mathematics: Teaching Developmentally* (1990). My version asks the children to take a handful of kidney beans (less than 100—we had practiced eyeballing 100 beans on our hundredth day of school) and count them, filling in the information in a table that started like this:

Number in group	Whole groups	Leftovers	How many all together
7			
3			
6			

The verbal instructions asked the children to put each new handful of beans into groups of whatever number was in the first column. For example, if the number in the first column was 7, they had to put their beans into groups of 7 and then fill in the rest of the information. I had chosen a variety of numbers to go in that first column, but I made sure that 10 appeared at least three times near the end of the sheet. The planned outcome was that the children would notice a pattern when they put the beans into full groups of 10—a pattern that didn't occur with any other number. I put the children into pairs and they set off to work.

As I circulated through the room, I noticed that the children were using several different strategies to accomplish their task. Kathy counted all the beans by ones. Jelani put the beans into groups and then counted, while Ellen decided to "make sure" and check Jelani's work by counting their beans again. Marc and Karla seemed to enjoy the challenge of taking more than 100 beans and were discussing their outcomes.

Building a System of Tens

Amy and Tuan were the first group I heard remark about the pattern they saw in the tens rows. They were discussing the fact that the number of whole groups and the number of leftovers turned out to be the number of beans that they had all together—that the number in the last column was a combination of the numbers in the previous two columns. At this point I also heard Kathy, who has a keen eye for patterns, make a similar observation.

Number in group	Whole groups	Leftovers	How many all together
3	7	2	23
7	5	5	40
10	6	7	67
10	3	8	38

The next day, the children finished their work and we came together to put our findings on a whole-class chart. The children offered examples of how to fill each line of the chart, and then I asked if they saw anything on the chart that they wanted to comment on. Many kids noticed what they came to call "the ten trick." I asked them why it worked.

Kimberly tried to explain what she understood: "The tens is what basically does it and the leftovers make it." Several other children tried to explain what seemed to be clear and yet confusing at the same time.

Eventually I asked, "Will it work with any other number of things in a group?" I expected their answer would be no, thinking only about groups of 10 and fewer, but I heard something different as the discussion continued.

Sean stated that he thought this "trick" would work with anything that had a 10 in it. I wasn't sure just what Sean meant, but several other children began to think about his comment and offered their ideas. Marc said that anything with a "one-zero" at the beginning would work. Sean responded that it worked with a hundred, a thousand, ten thousand, and a million.

Ellen said, "Fourteen groups of ten might not work." Most of the class agreed with this statement, but they weren't completely sure, so we all decided to test it. We took 14 groups of beans with 10 in each group, and I threw in a few leftovers. The children counted the groups by tens, and as we approached 140 the excitement mounted. I recorded our results on the chart and the class was abuzz.

Jelani said out loud, "Why does that work?"

Throughout the discussion, I was thinking about some of the ideas that had come up the week before while we were doing some mental math (arithmetic in our heads). The children had stated the following theory: "Ten plus any number less than 10 and more than 2 is a teen that has the same number at the end." Now I reminded them of their theory and asked if there was a connection between what we were seeing on this chart and that statement.

Marc's answer seemed to sum up my thoughts about teaching place value. He said, "There is a big connection, but I can't explain it."

C A S E **13**

Ones, tens, hundreds

Marie

GRADE 3, MARCH

We have been working on place value all year, while doing activities that range from counting on a hundreds chart to multiplying three-digit by one-digit numbers. In this lesson, my objectives were to revisit the writing of numbers, focusing on the value of the digits in the hundreds, tens, and ones places by using expanded notation, and representing these quantities with base ten blocks and by drawing pictures. Most of the children can write numbers. The confusion lies in representing the amounts. Here are some examples:

Lou showed 99 by laying out 9 rods (ten-sticks) and 9 units. His written number sentence to represent this amount was 99 = 9 + 9. His picture looked like this:

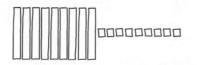

José wrote 730 = 70 + 30 + 0. He laid out 7 flats (100-squares) and 30 rods to show this quantity. Then he drew:

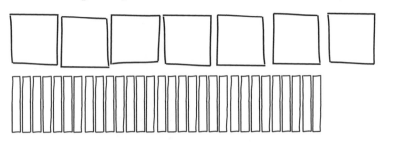

Mary showed 127 as one flat, 2 units, and 7 rods, which she arranged in the same order, as her picture shows. Her number sentence was 127 = 100 + 27.

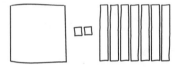

In another session I had the chance to talk with some of the children. Anne, Tia, Lou, James, Lee, and Darryl stayed with me while the rest of the class went to another activity. I gave out the papers and base ten blocks, and then gave each student a number to write down. The students each used the blocks to build their number, and then drew a picture of what they had built. Darryl's number was 237, which he showed by lining up 2 flats, 7 rods, and 3 units, in this order:

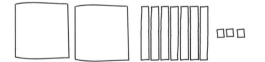

I asked him how he would form a group of 10 units.

DARRYL: Take 10 ones and stick them together to make a group of 10.

TEACHER: Lou, do you understand what Darryl said?

LOU: If he breaks up a 10 into 10 ones, it will still be 10.

Next, students picked their own number to represent. They made the same mistakes as before.

TEACHER: What is your number, Tia?

TIA: It's 426.

She laid out 4 flats, 6 rods, and 2 units, as shown.

TIA: [*Pointing to each block as she counts from left to right*] 100, 200, 300, 400, 401, 402 . . .

TEACHER: Why count the ones before the tens?

TIA: 400, 10, 20, 30, 40, 50, 60.

TEACHER: Where is the 60? [*Tia points to the 6 in 426.*] What does the 4 stand for?

TIA: 400.

TEACHER: The 2?

TIA: It stands for the ones.

I wrote 426 and circled the 26. Then I asked Tia what the number was, and she answered correctly.

Building a System of Tens

Who invented zero anyway?

Muriel

GRADE 2, APRIL

My second graders and I were looking at the hundreds chart set up in a 10-by-10 array. I had imagined leading a discussion toward the idea that moving down one space is actually adding 10. As we got into the discussion, I found that it is, of course, a complicated idea; even if I just tell my students that it works this way, they don't "get it" in any kind of meaningful way. Besides that, several of my students raised a very different idea—an idea about their understanding of zero. Following is a portion of our discussion.

1	2	3	4	5	6	7	8	9	10
11	12	13	14	15	16	17	18	19	20
21	22	23	24	25	26	27	28	29	30
31	32	33	34	35	36	37	38	39	40
41	42	43	44	45	46	47	48	49	50
51	52	53	54	55	56	57	58	59	60
61	62	63	64	65	66	67	68	69	70
71	72	73	74	75	76	77	78	79	80
81	82	83	84	85	86	87	88	89	90
91	92	93	94	95	96	97	98	99	100

Beth is describing for me—and anyone who is listening—why it works to move down one and actually add ten on this particular hundreds chart.

210

215

BETH: See the nines? [*She points to the column of 9, 19, 29, 39 . . .*]   220
This is 0 + 9, 10 + 9, 20 + 9, 30 + 9. The difference between 50
and 60 is 10, so the difference between 59 and 69 is 10.

Quite articulate, I think. Then Beth continues.

BETH: [*She points to 45.*] This has 4 tens and one 5. These [*pointing to
the columns with numbers ending in 6 or 7*] all have sixes,   225
sevens. [*Now she points to the 10, 20, 30 column.*] This one has
zeros. But these aren't quite zero, because. . . .

Her voice kind of trails off and my mind is racing. What did she say?
"These aren't quite zero"?

TEACHER: Because why? [*I am trying desperately to figure out in that*   230
moment all of what she is saying and trying to sort out what I
might ask next.]

BETH: Because if zero isn't here [*she points to 60*], then this 6 is only
6. It depends on where it [the zero] is. See, 15. [*She writes 15
on the board.*] This [*points to the 1*] is a 10, not a 1. Ten has   235
everything in it up to 9. The ten section has from 10 to 99.
The hundred section has—say it's one hundred and twenty-
five. [*She writes 125 on the board.*] But you don't write it as
100 or else it would look like this. [*She writes 100205 on the
board.*]   240

I'm in that place where I find myself spending a lot of time: hearing
many rich ideas, and wondering which ideas I should push on. I decide
to push on Beth's ideas about the zero thing.

TEACHER: You've written 125 separately, as 100205. But tell me some
more about zero.   245

BETH: It is sort of zero, but not exactly. [In 30] this zero makes it be
30. If this zero weren't there, it'd be 3.

YESSICA: I have something to say about how these zeros aren't really
zeros.

Attempting to include some other children in the discussion, I restate   250
what Beth has said, about the zero at the end of the number not being
quite the same as zero by itself. Yessica comes up to the board.

YESSICA: [*Writing 07 on the board*] That's 7. [*Now writes 0.7*] That's 0 point 7. [*And then she writes 70.*] That's 70. Zero represents 7 tens.   255

I am completely intrigued by these ideas and love the term *represents.*

TEACHER: So if this zero [*pointing to 0 in 70*] represents tens, in this number, 79, does the 9 represent tens?

BETH: Do you know what we really mean? Do you know the real thing?   260

    Lately Beth has been responding to my questions as if I did already know many of the answers I'm asking her to explain to me. I like to make my questioning as authentic as I can, but the fact is that I usually understand the mathematics that I'm asking the children to think through. Today my questions are framed to find out what the children are   265 thinking, to hear their ideas. I know that the 9 in 79 represents 9 ones, but I'm not sure what Beth thinks.

    I explain to her that in my math class for adults, we've talked a lot about zero and what it means to different people, and what it's worth, and whether it's odd or even, for example. And I express my honest   270 interest in what second graders think about zero. This is heard by several other people in class and they perk up a bit. The discussion continues.

YESSICA: On the calculator there's a 07.

TEACHER: And then is the 0 worth zero?

YESSICA: Yes. [*Other children nod in agreement.*]   275

TEACHER: But not in the 70?

YESSICA: Right.

BRIAN: For just 7, the zero doesn't have to be there, just the 7.

LAMONT: There are two ways to make zero. This is the 7 for the tens and it [the zero] makes 70.   280

TEACHER: What's the other kind of zero?

LAMONT: For the ones. [*He writes 08.*]

I'm thinking, "Two kinds of zeros? Wow."

BETH: It's like you sort of understand it, but nobody really understands it. Maybe someone will come around and figure it out. And who invented zero anyway?

285

I laugh and write the question on the board.

WENONA: Yeah, and who invented numbers anyway?

I write this down on the board also.

TEACHER: I need to see if I can find any information for you to read.

290

Several days later Lamont came with delight on his face to tell me that our librarian had seen the questions on the board and said she had a book called *Zero Is Not Nothing* (Sitomer, 1978). He eagerly went to the library to bring it back.

The next week, Henry came to me and said sincerely, "You see, Ms. Willis," holding his hands closed and then opening them palms up, "zero means there's nothing. See, there's nothing in my hands. That means zero."

295

I was thrilled that he had actually kept this issue in his head long enough to either talk to someone about it, or come up with that explanation on his own. It was also somehow very touching to me that he seemed to be gently offering me an explanation about something I didn't yet understand.

300

I guess I've written up this episode for a couple of reasons. One is simply that I love the idea that even a few of my second graders can have this kind of discussion about number. This kind of "chewing" on ideas is exactly what I most hope and work for in my mathematics (actually any subject) class. I am genuinely intrigued to have this window into some second graders' thinking about what zero is. I also am thrilled that the assertion is in the air that someone invented this zero thing, as well as the particular numbers that we use. It makes them much more accessible and "touchable."

305

310

I also wonder how making sense of zero affects children's understanding of place value. Actually, it's probably more to the point to wonder how *not* making sense of zero affects children's understanding of place value.

315

I am sometimes just overwhelmed with the range of ideas that bombard me in a relatively short discussion.

One hundred ninety-five

Danielle

GRADE 1, APRIL

In my classroom we do work on estimation, which gives the children experience in making reasonable guesses as well as the opportunity to count objects. Last week, we were working with a bag of jelly beans. The students were trying to guess how many jelly beans they could hold in one hand, and then compared that to the actual amount they could hold. We also discussed whether the amount would be the same every time they took a handful. Then we estimated the amount of beans in the whole bag. After we all made our predictions, I opened the bag and spread the jelly beans on a flat surface, to give the children the chance to decide if they were satisfied with their estimate, to adjust it if needed, and to say if it was too high or too low.

The children in my class had not done any formal work with place value, although we had counted objects well beyond 100. Several times students had asked how to write a number greater than 100 and I had showed them. But as of yet, we hadn't discussed numbers containing three digits. As we finished up with the jelly-bean counting, we learned that the bag contained a total of 195 jelly beans. I asked if anyone knew how to write that number using numerals. Suggestions included the following:

1095

10095

195

1395

1295

The children who gave the first two responses were able to explain them somewhat. They heard "hundred" and remembered something about 100 and zeros. They couldn't be more specific than that. Nathan, who gave the third response, said 195 looked like that and he just knew it. The child who gave the fourth response said it was a big number and that's how you write big numbers. The child who gave the fifth response, Bethany, responded the same as the Nathan. (She usually repeats an answer after hearing someone else give it.)

I asked the children to look at these numbers, think about 195, and talk to each other to about it. I also said that one of these was the right way to write it with numerals.

The children explained their answers to each other and arrived at the conclusion that the correct written form is 195. I don't recall the entire discussion, but I do remember that 1395 and 1295 were immediately discarded because they never heard anything about 3 or 2 in the number.

Nathan, who was the first one to offer 195, was able to convince everyone that he was right, which, of course, he was. I was curious about how he knew this.

When I suggested to Nathan that we spend some one-on-one time discussing how he knew about 195, he was more than pleased to spend the time with me alone. As we sat down together, he was all smiles and wanted to show me how smart he was.

TEACHER: Show me how to write one hundred ninety-five. [*Nathan writes 195.*] Why this way?

NATHAN: I first thought it was [*writes*] 1095, but that would be ten hundred ninety-five.

TEACHER: Why?

NATHAN: Take away the 95 and the 1 and 0 is ten.

TEACHER: What made you think of writing 195?

NATHAN: When I see 100 and go up, you take away the zeros. When you go up 100, 101, 102, you keep going up. You take away the zeros.

TEACHER: Why do you do that?

NATHAN: If you don't take away the zeros it would be 10095. That would be 100 and 95 put on the end.

TEACHER: How do you know about numbers?

Danielle

NATHAN: I can count up to 500. [*Starts to count, says 49, 30, self-corrects to 50, 51 . . . At 235, I ask him to stop.*] 380

TEACHER: When you look at 195 [*I write 195*], what do the parts tell you?

NATHAN: [*Makes circles around the numbers.*] Nineteen—if you take away the 5, just plain 5. If you take away the 19 [*he writes 195 again and circles parts of it*], 95 or 19. The middle can go either way. Plain 1, if you take away the 95, says "hundred." 385

TEACHER: Can you write other numbers? [*I dictate the numbers 372, 249, 107, 950, and 401, and Nathan transcribes them this way: 372, 249, 1007, 950, 4011. Then he changes 4011 to 401, but doesn't comment on or change 1007.*] 390

I wish I understood better how to interpret what Nathan knew. It appeared that he had some initial thoughts about place value. For example, he saw that numbers have different values in different situations. How much did he understand about these values? A few weeks later, we were working with base ten blocks. Nathan was trying to figure out how many days were in summer. He knew right away that 30 was three rods. But in trying to add the days in June, July, and August, he needed to add 30, 31, and 31. He didn't use tens as he counted, but instead counted each individual space on the tens rod. Where do he and I go from here? 395

400

C H A P T E R

4

More on addition and subtraction of two-digit numbers

CASE 16	The pink way	*Lynn, Grade 2, May*
CASE 17	Subtraction and invented algorithms	*Lynn, Grade 2, April (one year later)*

Over the last several years, Lynn, a second-grade teacher, has been thinking hard about the issues explored in chapters 1–3. As she tries to sort out what her second graders need to learn, and as she reviews what she has done in different years, she poses big curricular questions for herself. What do second graders need to learn about adding, subtracting, and place value? What kinds of mathematical tasks will help them learn these things? And what is the role of the algorithms conventionally taught in the United States? In the first of these two cases, Lynn reviews what she has done in her first two years of teaching second grade and shares her current thoughts. In the second case, written one year later, she has different ideas.

Before taking on Lynn's questions for yourself, first examine her students' thinking. As you read the two cases, take notes on these questions:

■ How do the two groups of children in the first case experiment with different addition algorithms?

■ In the second case, consider second grader Fiona's work: Where does she get stuck and how does she sort herself out?

C A S E **16**

The pink way

Lynn
GRADE 2, MAY

As the end of my second year of teaching second grade approaches, I find myself consumed, again, with questions about what the children are thinking when they add and subtract with regrouping. These questions seem broad and deep, and range from the level of the individual child— "What *is* he thinking?"—to the level of math education in the United States—"Why is the entire nation seemingly committed to *the* algorithm, anyway?"

Last year, I used trading games (chip-trading and rods-trading) to get at the issues I thought were involved in regrouping. I taught the children how to play (roll the dice, take tens rods and ones rods to correspond to your roll, and represent your total with rods), making sure they knew to trade in 10 ones for a ten, and 10 tens for a hundred. Later, I gave them word problems that involved regrouping, thinking they would apply their new knowledge to solve them. I was dismayed to discover that very few, if any, children made the connection between trading in ones rods for tens rods and adding two-digit numbers whose ones columns totaled more than 10. Some of them did learn the algorithm—I think because they were able to remember the steps and wanted to do as they were told.

Building a System of Tens

I am not convinced that any of them really understood how quantities combine. Some of the children did not learn the procedure, despite an obvious desire to do well and please their teacher. Some children, when faced with a problem that involved regrouping, just stopped. Some added on, counting by ones. Some ignored the dilemma of having, for example, 15 in the ones column, and came up with solutions that did not make sense.

This November I taught the rods-trading game again. I did not dare *not* to. I was determined to find an effective way to help the children *connect* the game to the addition it is meant to represent.

It did not work. Every way I thought of to make the connection clear was so confusing to the children that they could not even understand how to "do" the paper, much less say, "Oh! This adding is just like rods-trading!" or "Oh! This rods-trading is the same thing as adding!" It was frustrating for me and bewildering for the children.

A significant difference this year was that I included lots of word problems along with rods-trading throughout the whole year. I did not try to get the children to use *the* algorithm to solve the problems, and I did not try to push the connection to rods-trading. Instead, I asked children how they solved the word problems—since they all did—and recorded their procedures on audio tape and on posters.

Rods-trading had no discernible impact on how the children thought about addition and subtraction problems. Some children, who could answer questions about how many tens, how many ones, location of the tens and ones, and so on, would still count by ones when solving two-digit addition problems. Those children who apparently had a deeper understanding of place value still added the way they always had: tens first, and then the ones. They would occasionally use the words *trade in* to describe how they dealt with having more than 10 ones. Some children could not answer questions about where the tens and ones were, or did not understand what counting by tens really meant.

For a while, we left trading games and regrouping as a topic and worked on other things. Our math topics for the next several months included geometry and many, many word problems.

Then it was May and I felt the need to revisit the algorithm somehow. My thinking went something like this: Third grade approacheth. It is not up to me to say that we will all abandon the conventional algorithm. The children will be expected to know it. If I don't teach it to them, someone else will, perhaps wondering why I didn't do my job, which means now *they* have to, and now they're way behind, and the kids will test poorly the next year in fourth grade.

At some point I would like to have a discussion with my colleagues about the algorithm and the ways kids solve problems. I fantasize that we will all agree that children should be encouraged to think flexibly and solve problems in ways that make sense to them and in ways that they can explain without saying, "and then you do this because my teacher said to." This fantasy leads me to worry that parents and administrators both might question the whole school's approach and try to get people fired, while some parents decide to send their kids to private schools.

Meanwhile, I am still facing the end-of-year dilemma over the algorithm, so last week I prepared to approach addition with regrouping again. I made a poster showing five different methods of adding 38 and 25, each method written in a different color. The first four were methods that second graders had articulated when explaining their thinking in November; three of these (the green way, blue way, and red way) involved adding the tens first. The purple way showed counting on from 38 by ones. And, finally, the poster showed the traditional algorithm, in pink.

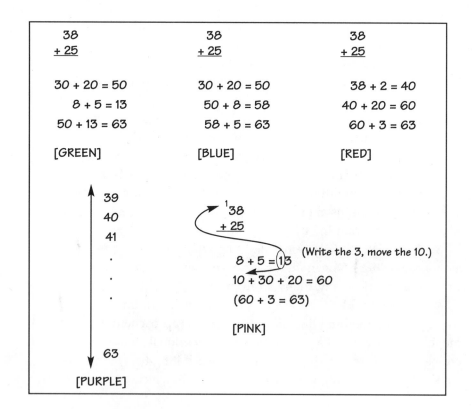

I met with a group of ten children who could solve regrouping problems pretty easily. I gave them the following word problem, asking them to pay attention to how they solved it and to please write something that would explain their thinking.

> **?** Ms. Kosaka and Ms. Rivest were watching kids playing outside. They counted 38 children in and around the climbing structure. They saw 25 kids playing freeze tag on the field. How many kids did they see?

The children got right to work and solved the problem quickly. They were eager to explain their thinking, anticipating what I usually ask them to do. They seemed slightly miffed that, no, I did not want to hear their ideas right off; I wanted to show them something first. However, when I told them that I had listened to a tape of second graders explaining their thinking earlier in the year, in order to make a poster of different ways kids solve problems, they felt sufficiently represented to listen. When I showed them the poster, they excitedly said, "I did it that way!" or "I solved it the green way!" This was actually a change from earlier in the year, when each child seemed invested in having his or her way be a little bit different from everyone else's.

We looked at the methods shown on the poster, trying to understand what was happening in each. Out of the ten children, eight solved the problem by adding the tens first, so we started with those three methods. Then we turned to the pink way, the traditional algorithm. One child, Wayne, had solved the problem using the traditional algorithm. He did not know that algorithm in November; when parents help children with homework, they often teach them the algorithm, so I assume that's how Wayne had learned it. Zack, who usually used that algorithm, did not this time. Another child, Eric, said that his grandmother had tried to show him the pink way. So we looked at the pink way and tried to make sense of it.

Wayne described how he used it. He said he started with the ones, adding 8 and 5 to get 13. Since you can't write 13 in the ones, you write the 3 there, and put the 1 over the tens. Then you add the tens, which is 60, so the total is 63. When I asked him why you can't write 13 in the ones, he said because "fifty-thirteen" doesn't make sense. Jamal added that 513 looks like five hundred thirteen. I asked, "What is this 1?" indicating the "carried" digit. Jamal said it was the ten from 13.

The other children in the group seemed to be following the discussion and were making comments. There was consensus in the group that this method was a weird way. Adam said, "That's way harder. Why would anyone do it that way?" The group agreed, and there were murmurs of "I'm just not going to learn it," and "Me either."

This was a painful decision point for me. I had gone into the lesson with fairly clear goals. I wanted the children in this group to think flexibly and solve these problems several different ways, one of which should be the conventional algorithm. I wanted them to know the algorithm for third grade and beyond, although I did not want to place *more* value on it than on the other methods. But the very fact that I was thinking they should solve problems lots of different ways, one of which had to be "the pink way," automatically placed too much value on this new, weird method, one that did not come from the students. I actually had conflicting goals between validating all the different methods of adding and wanting to be sure that everyone learned *the* algorithm.

I ended up saying something like, it was wonderful how they had ways of thinking that made sense to them, and that they were able to stretch their brains to understand how someone else was thinking. I added that I did want them to stretch their brains further and try to figure out this new method, partly because some adults and teachers would expect them to know it. Gulp. Their response was interesting. They wondered why some teachers thought this was the "best" way, a translation they made, of course, despite my delicate phrasing. They decided that it was *because* this way is harder, and therefore "more math-y." Now that they were older and smarter, went their reasoning, they should do things a harder way. I often tell them that I give them hard work because it stretches them, and that they are able to do it; when work is just hard enough they do their best learning. But learning an algorithm for something they can already do in a very meaningful way, an algorithm that in fact obscures the mathematics of combining numbers, seems to be an unnecessary complication, rather than a stretch to higher-level thinking. I think.

Anyway, next I gave the children another word problem and told them I wanted them to solve it using at least two different methods. They attacked it with gusto. Most of them tried the pink way as one method. Many of the children used all the methods shown on the poster. What amazed me was that they could all make some sense of the pink way.

I am not saying that the whole group now knows and understands that algorithm, but during this math period they were all able to use it to add 49 and 39. They talked to each other and helped each other. Some children wrote the numbers side by side instead of in vertical columns and got confused. Others wrote the numbers vertically, but left out the line that separates the addends from the sum. Yet they all found a way into the procedure and how it works.

I remember despairing last year because the children had been pretty consistently perplexed by what I wanted of them during trading games and this adding process. They had been hard-working and conscientious children in general, but most of them did not understand how this algorithm relates to addition, or place value, or trading.

I think a very important difference this year was that by the time these ten children were exposed to the traditional algorithm, they had success-fully constructed their own understandings of addition with regrouping. They were comfortable thinking of numbers in terms of tens and ones; this had meaning for them. Therefore their task was different. Now I was asking them to reconcile a new method with what they *already knew.* Last year, on the other hand, I had been wanting the class to construct an understanding of tens and ones, how numbers are made up, and how numbers combine, all at once—using one particular method that made no sense to them.

And what about the other twelve children in my class this year? I have many children whose grasp of tens and ones and of place value is less developed than it is for the ten children I met with initially. Given the same word problem, several of the remaining kids started at 38 and counted on 25 by ones. Two made Unifix cube collections of 38 and 25 and counted the whole thing by ones. A couple of them successfully added the tens and added the ones, but were frozen when faced with 13 ones. All these children can identify the tens place in a two-digit number. They can say how many tens and how many ones there are. They under-stand counting by tens at some level. But they do not use this knowledge when adding two-digit numbers.

Heather was laboriously counting on by ones to solve a word problem that involved adding 49 and 39. Someone near her suggested that she "use tens and ones." Heather said, "Oh, yeah!" and added the tens. Then she added the ones. Then she combined them. She did not seem confident or comfortable, but she did it. I wonder, though, what she was thinking. Her initial impulse—to count on—made sense to her, because that was what the problem suggested to her. She would probably have been sure that what she was doing represented the story in the problem, and that her result was the right answer. It seemed as if her friend's suggestion triggered her memory of a procedure, but I am not at all convinced that she was sure the "tens and ones" procedure matched counting on or the story problem in any way.

So, why would I want to require someone to add the ones first and then the tens when they have no impulse to think of a number in terms of tens and ones in the first place? Many of my children are still working on constructing a system of tens and ones. Until they do, the traditional algorithm will not make sense to them.

C A S E **17**

Subtraction and invented algorithms

Lynn
GRADE 2, APRIL (ONE YEAR LATER)

Every time we work on it, I think my appreciation for the complexities of subtraction increases. My students have been solving word problems involving two-digit addition and subtraction both with and without regrouping. They have been working on explaining and recording their processes for solving the problems. Our work with addition has been interesting and satisfying, and, as I find every year, subtraction proves to be more problematic than addition for seven- and eight-year-olds.

One word problem involved pigeons in the park: First there were 39 of them, and then a dog came along and 17 flew away, the question being, how many pigeons remained? Children solved this problem in an even wider variety of ways than I anticipated. As they worked and described their thinking, and as they tried to understand each other's thinking, the issue of how to keep track of what was going on kept arising.

Many children counted back from 39 to solve the problem. When they did so, several of them had to pause along the way. Isabel counted on her fingers, and at first didn't know when to stop. She seemed to lose sight of the 17 she was counting back to represent the departed birds, and therefore wasn't sure when she got to the remaining birds. She was, however, able to start over with a little more clarity and figure out how to use her strategy successfully.

Some children also counted up from 17 to 39. At least one child, Sabrina, then pronounced the answer to be 39, rather than 22. At least part of her confusion could result from not being able to hold in mind all at once both the original problem and the meaning of her numbers and procedures. When children count up to join two numbers, the last number they say is the answer; that's probably why Sabrina thought 39 was the answer.

Children who used more complex strategies also seemed to have trouble keeping in mind both the meaning of the numbers and the problem context. They also had trouble keeping track of numbers they had taken apart for their calculations. Fiona worked on a variation of the word problem that involved regrouping (of 37 pigeons, 19 flew away). She dropped the 7 from the 37 for the time being. She then subtracted 10 from 30. Then she subtracted 9 more. She puzzled for a while about what to do with the 7 now that she had to put it back somewhere. Should she subtract it or add it? I asked her one question: "Did those 7 pigeons leave or stay?" She said they stayed, and added the 7.

$37 - 19$

$30 - 10 = 20$ $\qquad$ $20 - 9 = 11$ $\qquad$ $11 + 7 = 18$

It was interesting to me that Fiona needed only that one question to clear up her confusion, and I think for the most part she subtracts this way and keeps it straight. While Fiona goes through the steps in her algorithm she is able to keep track of when to add and when to subtract. The 7 gets subtracted (from 37) and then added again (at the end, to 11). The 9 from the 19 is, in a way, added to the 10 in 19, but it is subtracted, because Fiona needs to subtract all of the 19. The 7 is part of what is being subtracted from. The 9 is part of what is being subtracted. It is a complicated process and it is amazing to me that a second grader can make sense of it for herself. I had a student last year who struggled with this very issue for weeks and never figured it out.

Paul also takes numbers apart to subtract. To solve $39 - 17$, he takes the 17 apart in three steps:

$39 - 10 = 29$ $\qquad$ $29 - 4 = 25$ $\qquad$ $25 - 3 = 22$

Paul keeps track of the 17 while breaking it into familiar chunks. Many children wondered where he got the 10, 4, and 3 from. How did he know what to subtract? How did he know when he was done?

Interestingly, Paul himself had questions for Nathan about how Nathan knew which numbers to put together for his answer. Here is Nathan's process for 39 – 17:

17 + 3 = 20

20 + 10 = 30

30 + 9 = 39

3 + 10 + 9 = 22

Nathan nearly always adds, even for a straightforward separating situation like birds flying away. After Nathan explained how he solved this problem, Paul said, "But how does he know what numbers to add up at the end?"

I thought a little bit about the conventional algorithm. A few children use it sometimes, ever since I gave word problems for homework. So much for asking parents not to help them. If a child memorizes the procedure, there is no real "keeping track." They must learn the steps, but they do not need to keep track of what the 3 in 37 means or how much of the 19 they have subtracted so far. All they do is use the recipe. If they get confused or forget a step or go out of order, children using this procedure tend not to go back and make sense of the numbers or the problem, or try to keep track of what is going on. I am not sure if this is unique to this algorithm, or if it happens because they have learned a procedure with no meaning in it.

Finally, an almost unrelated observation: This year for the first time I have never seen a single child "subtract up" in the ones column if the bottom number is greater than the top one. In other years, I have always had many children do this.

```
  37
– 19
  22  because 3 – 1 = 2 and 9 – 7 = 2
```

I am not sure what to make of this, but I hope it is because this year the children carry more of the meaning of the problem with them, which they do because they are allowed to construct their own ways of solving it.

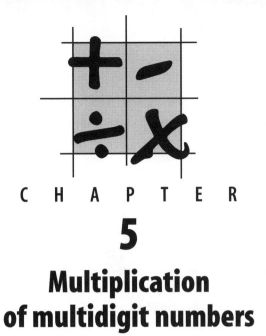

C H A P T E R

5

Multiplication
of multidigit numbers

This casebook began with a look at children's various methods for adding and subtracting multidigit numbers. This led to questions about how children come to understand the structure of multidigit numbers and how they can apply that understanding when they add and subtract. Now we ask a similar question about multiplication: How can large numbers be decomposed and recombined in order to multiply them?

In the four cases of chapter 5, we observe students working on multiplication in a variety of contexts. The first teacher, Eleanor, poses multiplication problems to the class without suggesting any particular approach. The second teacher, Lauren, has the children thinking in terms of clusters of related problems (cluster problems also appeared in Janine's case 5). Lauren also introduces the use of arrays. In Susannah's class (case 20), the children are working to remember the steps of the traditional algorithm. One year later, the same teacher experiments with a new way to approach multi-digit multiplication.

So that you can follow carefully the reasoning students are using in these cases, you might first work with various models of multiplication for yourself. For example, how could you draw a diagram, or arrange manipulatives, to represent 16×18? Do such representations suggest ways in which you might decompose the numbers to make the multiplication more manageable?

As you read the cases, take notes on the children's methods.

C A S E   18

27 x 4, or dogs looking for scraps

Eleanor

GRADES 3 AND 4, DECEMBER

While working on multiplication with the nine- and ten-year-olds I teach, I am trying to discover what signs and landmarks will tell me when they are ready to move beyond multiplication. That is, when do these children understand multiplication well enough, and just how do nine- and ten-year-olds understand it?

As part of their multiplication work, I have asked kids to work with arrays, to play games with them, to study them. We have had discussions about the operations and how to use them flexibly—choosing to use addition and multiplication in the same problem, depending on the numbers. We have talked about multiplying two-digit numbers and where addition and subtraction come into play. We have used base ten blocks and graph paper. The children have written story problems based on math sentences I gave them, and they have responded with math sentences based on story problems I have written.

Eleanor

Recently I gave eight children a page, for homework, that asks them to solve 27×4 in two different ways. In their written work, I found more clues about what they are understanding now.

Mark wrote:

First way: I added all the 20s which got to 80 and then I added four sevens and got 108.

Second way: I added the 20s but then I realized a shorter way than adding. I just did 4×7 which is 28 so $80 + 20 = 100$ plus 8 more is 108.

Joel wrote:

First way: Well, $2 \times 27 = 54$, so $54 + 54 = 108$.

Second way: First I added up all of the 20s and got 80 and then I added up all the sevens and got 28 and then I added 80 to 28 and got 108. [*Joel also added little notes that $4 \times 20 = 80$, and $4 \times 7 = 28$, and $80 + 28 = 108$.*]

Stephan wrote:

First way: I used my head only. I added 27 and 27 and I got 54, then I added 54 and 54 and I got the answer 108. I added 27 and 27 because I knew it was half of 4×27, so I put the two halves together and I got 108.

Second way: I knew that 27 was 20 plus 7 so I multiplied 4×20 and I got 80. Then I added 4×7 (and I got 28) to 80 and I got 108.

Jen wrote:

First way: $2 \times 27 = 54$ $2 + 2 = 4$ $4 \times 27 = 108$
$54 + 54 = 108$
I found out that $2 \times 27 = 54$ and then I added $54 + 54$.

Second way: $20 \times 4 = 80$ $7 \times 4 = 28$
I did $80 + 28$.
20×4 and 7×4 and then added them together.

Mika used similar strategies; she also pointed out that $4 \times 25 = 100$ and $2 \times 4 = 8$, so $100 + 8 = 108$.

The rest of the children's responses were very similar to these; all seem reasonable and thoughtful ways of going about multiplying in this instance. Looking overall at the integration of fact and facility, I see that the children are well on their way to understanding multiplication.

I have watched with particular pleasure the development of Jen's thinking. Ten days ago I had given this same group a story problem about 14 people buying 16 things each. In her math log, Jen interpreted this problem as 14×16. She also wrote:

$$2 = 28 \quad 3 = 42 \quad 6 = 84 \quad 7 = 103 \quad 14 = 206 \quad 16 = 234$$

Jen's arithmetic is off, but her strategy is a good one, anyway. This week I gave the group a story problem Mark made up:

 One night 63 dogs were looking for scraps in people's garbage cans. Each dog got 12 scraps and then went home to bed. How many scraps did they get all together?

Jen went up to the board within minutes and wrote:

$$2 \times 63 = 126$$
$$4 \times 63 = 252$$
$$8 \times 63 = 504$$
$$12 \times 63 = 756$$

Jen shows great progress in the past two weeks; in the "dog scraps" problem, she is now using notation for multiplication in a way that states her ideas more powerfully; the notation is becoming a standard form for her. By adding the last two steps (4×63 and 8×63) together to find 12×63, Jen indicates a solid grasp of the idea that she can partition and regroup the 12.

Although there may have been other factors involved, Jen saw in the "dog scraps" question $8 + 4 = 12$ and used that. Yet in the "people buying things" problem, her approach was less direct. I wonder if the presence of such new material and so many ideas didn't give her too much to juggle. Had she found what 8 fourteens were, she might have simply doubled that and gotten her answer. Jen is a kid who often uses doubles as a working strategy; now that she has had some experience with multiplying, I think she might see that she could effectively use doubling in the "buying things" problem. I am fascinated by her work anyway, as I think that she is uniquely self-taught. I wonder what questions or problems I could pose for her to push her thinking.

So, back to the original question: When can I move beyond my concen- | 80
tration in this area of math? Before moving on, I would like to see that
each child is as solid in her or his thinking as Jen. What do I see in her
work that satisfies me her thinking is solid? There is a sturdiness to her
understanding of the "dog scraps" problem that is evident in her direct
steps, her direct notation, and her answer. I am satisfied that I can give | 85
Jen any multiplication problem now, and she will have a way of thinking
about the problem—her own algorithm with which to start. I am not yet
convinced that this is the case with the rest of the children in the group,
so we will do more. I would like to step up the quality of the story
problems I have been giving them, too. I feel as if the ones I have been | 90
offering are just standard number problems with a coating of words.

C A S E   **19**

Multiplication cluster problems

Lauren

GRADE 4, MARCH

We have been working with arrays and with multiplication cluster
problems to develop the idea that problems can be broken into smaller
parts, which are then solved and recombined to get the answer to the
original problem. I have given students clusters of related problems such | 95
as the following:

$$2 \times 4 =$$
$$3 \times 4 =$$
$$2 \times 40 =$$
$$20 \times 4 =$$
$$23 \times 4 =$$

Students solve the problems and tell how they could use one or more of the easier problems to help them solve one of the harder ones. The following response to this cluster is typical:

> I just knew the first two. Then 2×40 is like 2×4, but when you multiply the 4 by 10 to get 40 you have to multiply the answer by 10, too. So $2 \times 40 = 80$. And 20×4 is the same, but you multiplied the 2 by 10 instead of the 4. The answer is the same. For the last one I started with $20 \times 4 = 80$ and just added on 3 more fours to get 92.

Some of the children talk about "adding a zero" to a number when they multiply by ten. I'm not sure what I think about the language. It disturbs me, but the children seem to know what they mean. Another student used problems from the cluster to create big and small arrays to help solve 23×4:

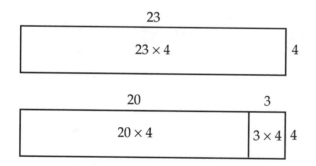

One day students made their own clusters. I presented a problem to be solved, and the students decided what other problems should be in the cluster to help someone solve the original problem. To start, I presented 21×4. The class suggested these for the cluster:

$20 \times 4 =$

$2 \times 4 =$

$1 \times 4 =$

No problem here, so I upped the ante with 271×7.

I heard Donte murmur, "It's going to be higher than 1,400." I repeated his comment and asked why. "Well, 200×7 will be 1,400 and there's still more you have to multiply." I asked for other estimates.

Howie said he thought it would be about 1,450 because "the first part would be like Donte's [*referring to $200 \times 7 = 1,400$*], and then there would be a 7×7 and a 1." Nobody commented at the time that it should be 70×7 instead of 7×7.

I asked if anyone could give me an estimate that would be close to the answer but more than the actual answer. There were a few attempts, but students couldn't explain where their estimates came from.

We then returned to creating the cluster. Jeannie volunteered the following:

$$200 \times 7 =$$
$$70 \times 7 =$$
$$1 \times 7 =$$
$$20 \times 7 =$$
$$2 \times 7 =$$
$$7 \times 7 =$$

We used the bottom three lines to help us solve the top two. Then we added the first three lines to get the product $271 \times 7 = 1{,}897$.

After we did another one together, I suggested that those who were ready to try this on their own could create and solve their own clusters. For the starting problem, the first number could have as many digits as they wanted, but the second number had to be a single digit. They were encouraged to discuss their work with others. Most students went off to try out their own problem-solving ability.

I was left with eight students who wanted more help. We worked through two more clusters together, then three of them went off to work independently. Two more had to leave the room for special programs. The remaining three students worked on and off with me and with each other at the board. These students had difficulty keeping in mind the place value for each digit. For example, they did not see the 7 in 72 as representing 70. They knew they were supposed to add some of the subproducts, but they were unclear as to which ones and why. I'm not sure how to help these children.

In the meantime, I started checking in with the other students. They were confident and excited to discover that they could multiply large numbers. Most students used a four-digit number for their first number. Although there were a few multiplication and addition errors, these students understood how to take the problems apart to solve them. Not all were as efficient as Jeannie's presentation on the problem we did together, but they were definitely headed in the right direction.

Marisa and Jiro understood how to take the problem apart but reverted to addition to solve $8,000 \times 6$ rather than relating it to 8×6.

Tynisha challenged herself with $92,512,995 \times 5$. She made two subproduct errors with order of magnitude. When I pointed out where the errors were made, she was able to correct them and proudly ended up with the right answer.

Amber and a number of others wrote down $5,000 \times 5 = 25,000$ without needing to write out 5×5, 50×5, and 500×5. Others, like Ricardo, wrote all the steps, either because they thought they were supposed to or because it was helpful to them.

Chantel and Tabitha attempted to solve their problems using the algorithm they had been taught the year before. Both had difficulty, but were able to solve the same problem correctly using clusters.

I was struck by how many students understood how to create their own clusters and how to use the clusters to solve hard problems. The students saw this as empowering. There was an air of excitement as they realized that they could tackle increasingly bigger numbers. Awed by Tynisha's accomplishment, a number of students tried really big numbers the next day. (A "really big number" seems to be defined as one that's too big for the calculator!)

I have some worries that the cluster method might become an alternate series of steps that students use without meaning. The small group that stayed with me was attempting to mimic what they had seen their classmates do, but clearly they did not have an understanding of the process. What can I do to build the foundation for these students? Should I provide more of the array activities and cluster problems, or something different? Should I have them build numbers with base ten blocks? Clearly, place value is a problem for them.

Do the successful students who "add zeros" when multiplying by ten or a hundred understand mathematically what they're doing, or only that it gets them the right answer?

I want to extend the estimating we did. I'd like students to be able to come up with a reasonable (and justifiable) range into which the answer will fall. This is a different, but related, way of looking at the magnitude of the numbers. Hopefully, students will use this information to evaluate their actual answers.

Full of enthusiasm, I tried the same "make-your-own-cluster" lesson with my other class the next week. It bombed! I realized I had not done as much groundwork to prepare them. Back to arrays and clusters!

Confusion over multiplication

Susannah

Learning and using multiplication is a big deal in third grade. The textbook, the students, the parents, and the fourth-grade teachers expect multiplication mastery by June. My students have been using multiplication concepts all year to calculate area and volume. They have also made graph-paper arrays, found patterns in the multiplication table, and done many other multiplication-related activities. As I remember what they have already done, I think the children understand what multiplication is and how the facts are derived.

But I wonder why it is still so difficult for them to learn the traditional process for multiplication computation. Even though the children can solve a problem using repeated addition, it is expected they be able to use conventional multiplication procedures. They can't always, and I don't know how to help them learn it! As I strive to make sure everyone really understands what they are doing, I even confuse the ones who can do the computation correctly. Help! This case is an anatomy of two students' confusions.

Given the problem 12×3, Michael said he would add 12 three times. I acknowledged that this was a good way to solve it, but asked him specifically to try multiplying instead.

Remembering some examples I had given of expanded notation as a way of understanding the multiplication process, Michael began by separating the 10 and the 2. Then he multiplied each number by 3, saying, "10 three times is 30, 2 three times is 6."

$$
\begin{array}{r}
1\ 12\ 2 \\
\times\ 3 \\
\hline
36
\end{array}
$$

"Wow, I really taught him how to make sense of this," I thought proudly, but prematurely.

This is how Michael solved the next problem:

$$2 \quad 2\!5 \quad {}^{1}5$$
$$\times 9$$
$$\overline{854}$$

"I separated the 20 over here [to the left] and the 5 over here [to the right]. First I multiplied 2×9 and got 18 so I put down the 8 and carried the one to the 5. Then I added $5 + 1 = 6$ and multiplied $6 \times 9 = 54$."

He did expand the number to see each part clearly, and he did get the number facts correct. That was the good news. The bad news was not only the illogical and incorrect answer, but the fact that Michael did the procedure with confidence even as he forgot about number value and placement. Was he just trying to imitate a meaningless process, or did part of this algorithm make sense to him?

Michael was experimenting with multiplication computation for the first time, but Lucinda, a bright and capable student in all subject areas, was already adept at these computations:

$$
\begin{array}{cc}
13 & 12 \\
\times\,3 & \times\,3 \\
\hline
39 & 36
\end{array}
$$

However, when given a problem with "carrying," here's what happened:

$$
\begin{array}{r}
1 \\
49 \\
\times\,2 \\
\hline
108
\end{array}
$$

She made the common mistake of multiplying 5 tens $\times$ 2 instead of multiplying 4 tens $\times$ 2 and then adding the additional ten. It was easy to get her to see her error; I asked her to add the two numbers and figure out what was really happening.

$$
\begin{array}{r}
49 \\
+\,49 \\
\hline
98
\end{array}
$$

This Lucinda did, and recorded her new answer:

$$
\begin{array}{r}
49 \\
\times\,2 \\
\hline
88 \\
+\,1 \\
\hline
98
\end{array}
$$

In anticipation of smooth sailing or, rather, smooth computing, I asked Lucinda to do 53×9. She did remember that the 2 (2 tens from $3 \times 9 = 27$) needed to be added rather than multiplied, but she lost track of the value of the 2 and placed it under the 400:

$$
\begin{array}{r}
53 \\
\times\,9 \\
\hline
457 \\
+\,2 \\
\hline
657
\end{array}
$$

Wanting her to judge the accuracy of her answer, I suggested that she make an estimate. Lucinda mentally computed 50 ten times as 500 and realized her answer was too large. She again recognized her error, "It's not 200, it's 20," and adjusted her figures.

$$
\begin{array}{r}
53 \\
\times\,9 \\
\hline
457 \\
+\,20 \\
\hline
477
\end{array}
$$

I should have stopped here and let her practice what she had learned, but Lucinda insisted that since her mother had taught her all about multiplication, I should give her "a real hard one." So I pressed on by having her try 29×15.

$$
\begin{array}{r}
29 \\
\times\,15 \\
\hline
105 \\
+\,4 \\
\hline
145 \\
+\,29 \\
\hline
174
\end{array}
$$

Again, an estimate gave her a hint that her answer this time was too small. I helped her see that, for her second subproduct, she was not multiplying by one, but by ten. Unfortunately, when she redid the computation with her new insight, "10 times 9 is 90, and 20 times 10 is 200," she wrote it this way:

$$
\begin{array}{r}
29 \\
\times\,15 \\
\hline
105 \\
+\ \ 4 \\
\hline
145 \\
+\,2090 \\
\hline
2235
\end{array}
$$

What should I do? Encourage the students to keep adding if that's what makes sense to them? (Rick attempted to solve a problem that ended in 500×4 by adding 4 five hundred times. I talked him out of it after we agreed it *would* give the right answer.) What representations would help the process become understandable? How do I lead the kids to develop a procedure that has meaning for them? How can I hold myself back from just explaining and then expecting them to imitate? Isn't that how I learned? How can I keep from befuddling those who can already do the computation?

C A S E **21**

Multiplication revisited

Susannah

GRADE 3, APRIL (ONE YEAR LATER)

It's that time of the year again when my third graders attempt (at my initiation) to transfer their knowledge of multiplication from concept to computation. Of course, we have been applying the ideas of multiplication all year, but now comes the challenge—for the students and for me to devise a multidigit multiplication procedure that is both meaningful and useful.

Susannah

This year, I determined, my instruction would be different. I borrowed an idea from Marilyn Burns (1987), who writes in *A Collection of Math Lessons*, "Before resorting to paper and pencil computation, I think it is important to deal with multiplication mentally" (p. 33). Some of the examples she suggested seemed hard for my students to do mentally ("How many legs on 36 dogs?"), but after translating her ideas into problems relevant to my classroom, I presented the following warm-up-and-stretch-your-brain activity. 290

 We need 4 dozen eggs for Easter and Passover celebrations. How many must we buy? 295

Some children used the tried-and-true method of adding, with quick and accurate results.

KANEISHA: I just doubled 12 to get 24 and then added 24 and 24 because that's four times, so 48. 300

Others were able to see the usefulness of breaking apart the numbers when I presented a problem with larger numbers.

 There were 64 teams at the beginning of the NCAA basketball tournament. With 5 players starting on each team, how many starting players were in the tournament? 305

"Wow, that's hard," proclaimed Debra loudly, and a chorus of protesters joined her. Undaunted, Laurel presented her thinking.

LAUREL: That would be 64×5. I use one 10 because I know $5 \times 10 = 50$. Then you do that six times. [*She counted by fives, not using her fingers, but moving her lips and nodding her head for each group of five.*] That's 30, I mean 300. Then you add 4 five times, which is 25, no 20. I added it all together and got 320. 310

Chris, usually reticent and lacking in confidence, volunteered his thinking in a quiet, unassuming voice.

CHRIS: 64 means $60 + 4$. [*Silently I rejoiced that all our practice parti- tioning numbers was not forgotten.*] So I did 60 five times, for 300. Then 4×5 is 20, so the answer is 320. 315

Chris returned to his seat in a way I can only describe as cocky. I was certainly impressed.

Jack, our resident goof-off but intuitive math thinker, explained his strategy next.

JACK: I split the 64 into four parts—20, 20, and 20. [*Four parts, I wondered? But I waited without interrupting.*] I did each one separately.

$20 \times 5 = 100$
$20 \times 5 = 100$
$20 \times 5 = 100$

Then the last part, 4×5, is 20. All together, 320.

These were the ideas and strategies I'd tried so hard to explain and instill in my students last year: breaking up numbers into useful parts, recognizing which numbers are being multiplied and by how much, finding a way to multiply that makes sense. Posing the right questions and relying on the children to use what they'd been practicing all year proved to be the solution to teaching multiplication. Of course, not everyone had moved beyond adding or understood what their classmates were doing. But they were listening and would begin to develop new strategies as we continued to multiply.

The warm-up part of the math period was finished, and I was just about to hand out colored tiles for building arrays, when another multiplication opportunity presented itself.

TEACHER: We have 18 kids here today, and each one needs 12 tiles for the next activity. How can we figure out the number of tiles to give out?

A second later I realized this problem was a leap from the ones we'd just done, but it was "real life," so I let the question stand. I was surprised that no one suggested using a calculator, their usual response to big numbers. But who needs a calculator when you have Josh!

JOSH: That would be 18×12, and I know 10×10 is 100 and 8×2 is 16, so if you add them together it would be $100 + 16 = 116$.

Everyone seemed satisfied with Josh's answer, whether out of agreement or lack of interest I wasn't sure. After all, the process mimicked what they'd just been doing. I was thinking about what to say that would help them see the error of their ways, when David's voice broke the quiet.

DAVID: That's wrong.   355

TEACHER: What do you mean, David?

DAVID: I did 18×10 and got 180, but I thought at first I was wrong, so I double checked. I noticed that Josh didn't do 8×10, so my answer was right. [*David is very knowledgeable about the workings of our number system, but leaves gaps in his verbal*   360 *explanations. His mind races, and neither his mouth nor our brains can keep up.*] I didn't do the 2 yet, so I do 18×2. Then you add it up—$180 + 36$.

"Wow," I thought. I was amazed at his understanding, but realized that the rest of the class looked dazed. Luckily, there will be more chances   365 for David and Josh and others to show what they know about multiplication. I'll leave them to it and go out to lunch.

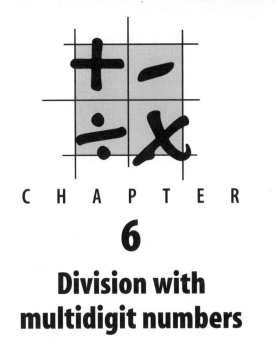

C H A P T E R

6

Division with multidigit numbers

In chapter 6, we look at division in terms of mathematical questions similar to those addressed elsewhere in this casebook. As you read the following cases, take notes on these questions:

- How can large numbers be decomposed and recombined in order to divide?

- How do the methods for dividing compare to those that can be employed for the other operations?

- What principles are shared across operations, and what principles are unique to each?

Although the children in the cases are in third to sixth grade, teachers of younger children can consider the following:

- What ideas are these children employing that can be developed at an earlier age?

- What do my students already understand about division?

- How can I help my students extend their ideas and build concepts that will support this later work?

C A S E   22

Exploring division

Betty

GRADE 6 (SPECIAL ED), NOVEMBER

Four special-needs students, Naomi, Eduardo, Maura, and Alma, had been taken from their class so that I could help them with division. While their teacher was working on division with her 25 sixth graders, these four students couldn't keep up.

I thought we would begin to explore division by "acting out" $72 \div 3$. I handed out base ten blocks and asked the students to show their thinking. Eduardo started out by writing the problem this way:

$$3 \overline{)72}$$

In the meantime, Alma counted 72 in base ten blocks (7 rods + 2 units) and put those in one pile. She then counted 3 units and put them in another pile. I asked her what the 3 was and Eduardo looked over. Although he could not articulate it, he knew something was wrong. He reached over and took the 3 away. I asked again what the 3 was, but Alma had no answer.

5

10

All the while, Naomi was busy jotting down a series of letters:

D
S
M
B

I asked the four children to turn their attention to the blocks that Alma had laid out. As we all sat there looking at them, I suddenly realized that I could not visualize the connection between the algorithm and the acting out of the solution! Since Alma was still confused about the 3, Maura suggested that we make up a word problem.

The 72 became pieces of candy and the 3 became people; they would share the candy equally among the people. I could really feel the group's thinking moving! Eduardo started to arrange units to represent the people, but he quickly saw the confusion this would cause when he went to deal out the candy. Instead he began to deal the "candy" to Naomi, Alma, and me. He gave us each 2 rods, traded the remaining rod for 10 units, and then dealt out the 12 units. At the end, we each had 2 rods and 4 units. The group agreed that 72 ÷ 3 = 24.

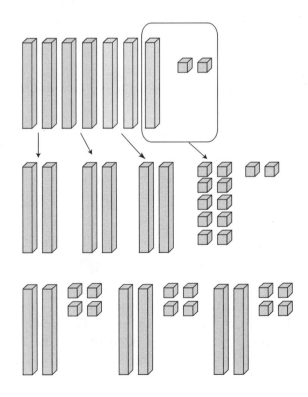

All this stimulated my own curiosity. How intriguing it was to see and experience the quantities by putting the numbers in a context! The question I had for myself was, How do Eduardo's actions relate to the long division algorithm that these children are supposed to learn?

Alone at the end of the school day, I get out the base ten blocks and sit down at a table. First I take 7 rods and 2 cubes—72 pieces of candy to be shared among 3 people. This time, I am concentrating on the word problem in conjunction with the algorithm and the steps we teach. How are they connected? I write out the problem in traditional form:

$$3\overline{)72}$$

We teach the children four steps in the long-division algorithm (Naomi's "DSMB"):

1. Divide
2. Multiply
3. Subtract
4. Bring down

OK, here's the first step: 3 divides or "goes into" 7 how many times? I'm dividing 72 pieces of candy among 3 people. It's not 7, but 70. If I think

$$3\overline{)7}$$

then I'm thinking of 7 rods, and there's a remainder of 1. If I think

$$3\overline{)72}$$

there is a remainder of 1 ten.

Step 1, I can see and understand.

Step 2, multiply. What is going on here in acting out division?

$$3\overline{)7}^{\,2} \qquad 2 \times 3 = 6$$
$$\phantom{3\overline{)}}6$$

In the *action* of division, I can see that 3 groups of 2 rods *does* equal 6 rods.

Step 3, subtract. All right—I started out with 7. I made three groups with it. So I took, in effect, 6 away from my original group of 7. That's the subtraction in action: In dealing out the 7, the three groups each got 2. That means I gave away 6 and have 1 left over. But wait a minute! Did I deal out 7 pieces of candy? I don't think so. That 7 meant 70. And the 1 left over is 1 rod, which stands for 10 pieces of candy.

    Step 4, bring down. When I trade the rod for 10 units, I bring in the other 2 units and have 12. And now I put those in three groups.

    At this point I have to say I still feel fuzzy about the relationship of the algorithm to the *action* of division, even though when I have both the algorithm and manipulatives side by side, I can see relationships.

65

70

C A S E   **23**

Discussing division

Eleanor

GRADES 3 AND 4, OCTOBER

This case describes my initial discussion of division with a math group of eight- and nine-year-olds. To begin, I wanted to know what the children had to say about the topic itself.

TEACHER: Well, what is dividing?

Mika spoke right up and contributed the first idea.

75

MIKA: Taking one number and making it into more than one part. Like 9 into 3 parts.

STEPHAN: Taking a number and splitting it. Like 9 divided by 3, by 2— would be equal. [*pause*] Actually, well, you can't do that.

    This idea that dividing is locked into splitting numbers in half seems to keep creeping into discussions as the days go by. Is it a confusion in the way some children visualize division?

    Jen heard Stephan's confusion and tried to help clarify and articulate his thinking.

80

JEN: Split one [a 9] in half so it's 4 and $\frac{1}{2}$. Like there is the 4 and the 4 and then one more, and that would be $\frac{1}{2}$, so it's $4\frac{1}{2}$. [*I know she means that she instantly sees the possibility of dividing an even number, 8, in half, and then the leftover 1 in half, to make $4\frac{1}{2}$.*] | 85

MARK: Sometimes you can't split a number in half. Like 5 pieces of—well, metal or something. | 90

TEACHER: Well, how about chairs? Take 5 chairs.

MARK: Yeah, like if there were 5 chairs and we [*pointing to his neighbor*] both wanted them, it wouldn't work. If you can split it in half, it's like dividing. | 95

TEACHER: Sagel, you were teaching Stephan your strategy for dividing by 2 the other day. Can you talk about your system?

SAGEL: I think it was 74, but let's say you had 8 and you divided it, so I would draw a line and call it 1, and here, and call it 2, and here, and call it 3, and 4, 5, 6, 7, 8. | 100

Sagel demonstrated the strategy, drawing tally marks on the board, alternating between two rows:

| | | |

| | | |

At this point I decided to give the group a problem and see what would happen. I asked them to divide 364 by 2. I thought that giving the children a large number might elicit more sorting out than a smaller one, | 105
and dividing by an even number would let them start from what they "know" about dividing. Jen went to the board.

JEN: 364, well, I take the 64 away. [*She hides it with her hand and pantomimes putting it on the other side of the board but doesn't write anything yet.*] It's 300. I split $\frac{1}{2}$ of 300 and it's 150. Then I | 110
bring back 64 and cut it in half. It's 30 and I put aside the 4. Then that's 2, so it's 182. [*She writes 182 on the board.*]

MARK: She did it exactly the way I do it.

TEACHER: Mark, why don't you try 496 divided by 4?

MARK: First I'll take away 96 so I have 400. Then I'd do what equals 400, so it's 200, and then half of that is 100, so it's 100. Then I have to put back the 96 and divide 90 but that's 50 and 40? What do I do? Um.

JEN: It's 45.

MARK: Oh yeah, that's what I was going to do. I would add the 5. But so then I divide 45 in half and it's 22 and [*pause*] $\frac{1}{2}$. Then I go back to the 6. Six divided by 2 is 3 so it has to be $2\frac{1}{2}$ — no, I mean $1\frac{1}{2}$. So 45 + 24. [*He has added the $22\frac{1}{2}$ and the $1\frac{1}{2}$ for the 24 on the board.*] It's 69, so all together it's 169.

After Mark finished, the group talked about adding all the 100s contained in four 169s and decided that Mark had made a mistake. I pointed out that, in his long rendition, he added the 45 he had split into $22\frac{1}{2}$, but that was an error.

MARK: My work is always so messy.

This led to a discussion about recording and how important it is, when there are so many steps, to make accurate notes about the work so that steps can be followed or retraced.

JEN: Well, I write math sentences, but I never write them while I am doing the math because, by the time I write it down, I have forgotten what was really clear in my head. My work in my head is really neat, so I wait and write the math down after I have the answer. Unless I am drawing a picture.

MARK: I usually just add up everything anyway.

We talked for a minute about the possibility of doing any math problem by adding. Then I sent them off to work on some other division problems like the ones we had been doing ($64 \div 4$, $20 \div 5$, $121 \div 3$). The problems were just dividing-for-dividing's-sake problems, though I added something about chocolate chips or numbers of people to put them in a story context.

Eleanor

Kia broke down and cried when she couldn't divide 30 by 2 because she knows something about "odd numbers can't be split in two, and if 3 is odd, then you can't do the problem." A new kid in the class, Kia is extremely bright, but she has a lot of math rules in her head which aren't helping her much. Joel just whispered that he was completely confused. Mika and Jen skillfully divided three-digit numbers by 2, 3, and 4. Sagel and Stephan, the only third graders in the group, happily tossed the discussion of dividing into some deep recesses in their minds and instead added and added away. Mark gnashed his teeth with great spirit while trying to divide something into three groups. His strategy of dividing in half and then half again didn't work well for him. He really wanted to get it, and he pushed and shoved his way through the problem.

The discussion was interesting to me for a couple of reasons. Basically, I didn't like it at first, though in retrospect it feels like a glimpse into the repertoire of conversations that kids can have in the class, beyond discussions of math story problems and strategies for solving them. When I tried introducing "an action"—an operation—as a topic for discussion, I found it extremely difficult to balance and assist the kids in their thinking. The use of the operation was not imbedded in an ongoing problem; the subject was not raised by the kids themselves; and, for the most part, there was a lot of talking into the air from one kid and then another, not enough of a give-and-take discussion *about* something.

So what's the problem? Why does dividing feel like a missing-addend problem, but instead with a missing factor? Some of those kids could go off from that discussion and build on their strategies of dividing. What did they understand that the rest didn't? What allowed them to move forward when the others were so clearly reeling during the problem time we had after the discussion?

For 20 ÷ 5, Stephan wrote:

20 divided by 5 = 4. I counted up by 5 and I got 4.

For 64 ÷ 4, Joel wrote:

64 divided by 4 = $11\frac{1}{2}$.

I think Joel worked out $6 \div 4 = 1\frac{1}{2}$ and $4 \div 4 = 1$. Then he somehow combined $1\frac{1}{2}$ with 1 to get $11\frac{1}{2}$. For the same problem, Mark wrote:

16 + 16 = 32 + 32 = 64 . . . 16.

Jen's paper showed this work on two problems:

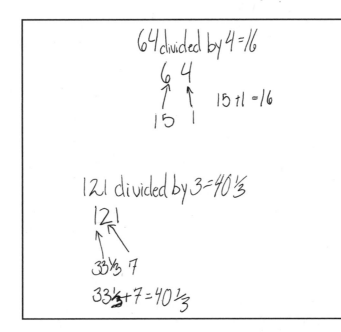

These kids are in really different places. Jen is able to hold onto true quantities, and they remain stable for her. She can see wholes and parts, and the whole picture is extremely clear. She has invented her own algorithms all the way along in math. (Having also taught her at age five, I remember with what great delight and humor she would make jokes at the snack table, substituting the word "eight" for the actual number of crackers, which was four, and calling everything that was really four "eight," just for the fun of it.)

Mark is adding; he is also stuck on dividing as splitting in 2 and powers of 2.

Joel does not appear to read the 6 in 64 as 60 when he gets into the division problem. He has divided 6 by 4 and 4 by 4, but then he just slips the digits together and calls the result $11\frac{1}{2}$.

Stephan is adding and making accurate estimations, but he is not clear about the idea of division as a way of taking numbers apart rather than building them up.

The information I glean from this episode helps me begin to understand what the children are working on. Division is not the most significant investigation at this point for every child in the class. I want to

Chapter 6

concentrate now on solidifying what numbers are made of and some of the ways in which numbers are organized in their behavior (odd and even in particular), and I can do that while simultaneously reaching toward division. I know that Jen, Art, and Mark have a lot to teach each other. Jen's grasp of numbers and intuitive understanding of factors will enable her to articulate what Joel may be speculating about. The notion of chunking numbers into multiples of fives, tens, and hundreds would be immensely useful to many of the children in the class, and I think the strategies would spread quickly if the right problems were offered. We can focus on the idea that the same numbers can stand for different quantities within the same problem, and on the idea that if you do something to one side of an equation, you need to do an equivalent action to the other side of the equation. At the same time, the children can be investigating the equivalency of operations and gaining fluency in those manipulations of number.

The following day we had parent conferences, and the number of parents whose children had come home and talked about this new idea named "division" was remarkable and surprising—especially because they spoke so positively! Joel's father said that, the night before, he had watched Joel solve a problem. Shaking his head, he said, "And there was this kid, sitting at the kitchen table, quietly inventing long division."

CASE 24

Sharing jelly beans

Janie
GRADE 4, APRIL

This week I decided to see what my fourth-grade students knew about division. I plan to concentrate more on division later in the year, but at this time thought I would just see what they already knew. I decided to throw out a problem and see how they tackled it.

> **?** How would you divide 134 jelly beans among 6 kids?

I told the students to pay particular attention to *how* they tackled this problem, and to write about some of the strategies they used. I asked them to work alone so we could see how many different strategies we could come up with. There was a wide range of strategies at the end of the period.

Some children drew pictures of 6 kids and, one by one, split up all 134 jelly beans.

José started with 100 beans and divided them up into groups of 25, "but this was only 4, so I kept going down until I had enough for 6 kids." He didn't say how he accounted for the other 34.

India first estimated how many each person was going to get, and then turned around and used the regular division algorithm.

Jamie started by giving each kid 10 jelly beans, then gradually increased each kid's share.

Mario first multiplied 6×20, and that gave him 120. Then he multiplied 6×2 and added 12 more for a total of 132. Then he divided the 2 extra jelly beans into 6 pieces and each kid got $22\frac{1}{3}$.

Most of the students grouped the jelly beans or estimated rather than doling them out one by one. I was pleased with that. I was also pleased at how many decided to try to split the last 2 jelly beans, rather than just disregard them.

April's strategies interested me and I wanted to hear more about how she tried to solve the problem. She started off by saying that "you have to know multiplication." She said that her first strategy was to pick a number and count up with it, but her second strategy was to put a two-digit number times 6 and see what the answer would be. I asked April to explain how she decided on a two-digit number, but she couldn't get past telling me the correct answer (22) and how that worked into the 134. To try to understand her thinking a little better, I asked her to work on another problem so she could talk a little more about how her strategy developed. I gave April the chance to pick a division problem, and she decided to use jelly beans again and make the problem a little harder:

? Divide 143 jelly beans among 8 kids.

I asked April to tell me first what she did when she was dividing. She said that division was putting things into groups. "You have to multiply the things to get the groups—like take 8 times any number and see what the answer is." She began her strategy by saying that she knew each kid would get more than 10 jelly beans because that would be 80, and that if each kid got 20 jelly beans, that would be 160, which was too much. So she knew two things: that 10 was too small and 20 was too big. I asked if she thought the correct number would be closer to 10 or closer to 20. She said she thought it would be around 14, and proceeded to multiply 14×8 to get 112. She then said that you had to add 31 more.

I could tell that she was getting confused with all the numbers, so I tried to make it easier for her by setting up a system to keep track of them:

She then decided to try 22×8 and got 176. She said she knew she had to try a number that would bring her close to the 160 mark, but lower.

April now decided to "bag" this idea and came up with another strategy—to see how many eights were in 100, and then how many eights were in 43—to see if that worked. Her process:

$10 \times 8 = 80$, $11 \times 8 = 88$, $12 \times 8 = 96$ (with 4 left)

$5 \times 8 = 40$ (with 3 left)

The next part she struggled with. She was losing her train of thought and was confused by all the numbers she had just generated. I tried to help her sort out what she had done by showing her that she had found 12 groups of 8 in 100 and 5 groups of 8 in 40, and that in both cases she had numbers left over. I asked her to think about how many groups of 8 she had. She had 17 groups of 8 (which totaled 136) with 7 jelly beans left over. Good.

Then she came up with a way to divide up the 7 extra jelly beans. She took 4 of them and divided each in half, so each of the 8 kids got $\frac{1}{2}$. Then she had 3 left over, so she took 2 of those and divided them into fourths, so each kid got an additional $\frac{1}{4}$. Then she divided the last jelly bean into eighths, so each kid got another $\frac{1}{8}$.

Now the question was, How much was $\frac{1}{2} + \frac{1}{4} + \frac{1}{8}$? This is how she solved that problem:

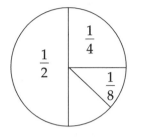

April was delighted when she saw that $\frac{1}{8}$ was left over; she immediately knew that the total was $\frac{7}{8}$. In the end, each kid got $17\frac{7}{8}$ jelly beans.

I was impressed with April's strategies and with how well she could explain what she was trying to do. I was impressed by her ability to change strategies when one didn't seem to be working for her. I was also impressed with the ease with which she was able to combine the fractions, even though we hadn't done much of that in our fraction unit.

The next day, Jorge came in with a problem that he said his father wanted us to try—a special challenge. I'm not sure if it was really his father's problem, but we accepted the challenge. His problem was 1007 divided by 9. At first the problem seemed difficult, but within a few minutes, *many* of the children solved it. Juanita was proud of her strategy and explained it to the class: She knew that $100 \times 9 = 900$ and that $10 \times 9 = 90$, so that took care of 990. She then added one more 9, for 999, which gave everyone 111 jelly beans to start with. She now had 8 more, which she divided into *ninths*, and arrived at her answer of $111\frac{8}{9}$.

I was surprised at how natural this process was for these students. In the past, I would have taught the traditional algorithm, which would have given them little in the way of understanding. Now they had their own methods, many of which involved dividing things up into large chunks first, then gradually decreasing the size of the chunks. Some still struggled with smaller numbers, and it was awkward dealing with the different levels in the class, but they were still arriving at the answer *their* way and with a greater understanding of the process. By observing their processes and listening to their strategies, I feel that most have a very good understanding of what division involves, and have a variety of means available to them to help solve this type of problem.

Janie

My question now: At what point do I teach them a shortcut—or do I? Do I encourage them to invent their own algorithm? Or do I leave them to refine the methods they are using now? Do I show them the method by which I learned division (and taught division for most of my teaching days—and, oh yes, I agree—without teaching much in the way of understanding), or do I continue to let them use their own process in spite of how slow it may be? I know the philosophy; I understand the philosophy; I agree with the philosophy. But once they understand the concepts, is there ever a place for the traditional way? This is a real question.

Now that our testing period is finally over, we are back to work on division again. I still feel the need to simplify the students' process of division, and I am still torn about introducing the traditional algorithm as a means to do this. This week I told my class about this dilemma. I told them that the way I learned to do division in my elementary grades did not help me at all understand what I was doing, and that I wanted them to come up with a way (or several ways) I could teach a division algorithm in the future that would let kids understand division. I gave them another problem and asked them to work on it—first individually, and then with a partner, if they wanted to.

Andy seemed very restless and uninterested in the task, so before he disrupted the work of his group, I asked him if he and I could work together. I asked him to think about the problem while I got everyone else started. When I returned to work with him, he said he was thinking about doing the problem 453 ÷ 6 as a bar graph. I had no idea what he was getting at, but he drew a chart with six columns.

I was interested to see how Andy was going to use his "bar graph." He told me that next he was going to draw pictures of the hundreds, tens, and ones using "those place-value blocks." Below the chart, he drew something like this:

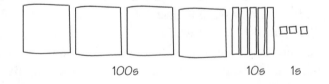

100s   10s   1s

After Andy drew his pictures, he realized that he couldn't give each of the 6 people 100, so he split each of the hundreds into 50 and 50. When he gave each of the 6 kids 50, he wrote this information on his chart.

50	50	50	50	50	50
1	2	3	4	5	6

Number of kids

I could now see how he was using his "bar graph"—not a bad way of organizing his numbers! This took care of 300; he now had 100 + 50 + 3 left to divide up. He proceeded to cut the last hundred into tens; he now had 10 tens + 5 tens + 3 ones. He knew that with 15 tens, he could give each kid 2 more tens, so he added this to his chart.

Andy now had 3 tens and 3 ones left. He said that 3 tens equals 30, and 30 divided by 6 is 5, so he gave each kid 5 more and added this to the chart. He now only had 3 left, so he split each in half and gave each kid $\frac{1}{2}$ more. Looking back at the chart, he could now say that each kid got $75\frac{1}{2}$. (Notice that he personalized the problem—at first he didn't talk about a context, but now he talked about each kid getting a certain amount.)

$\frac{1}{2}$	$\frac{1}{2}$	$\frac{1}{2}$	$\frac{1}{2}$	$\frac{1}{2}$	$\frac{1}{2}$
5	5	5	5	5	5
10	10	10	10	10	10
10	10	10	10	10	10
50	50	50	50	50	50
1	2	3	4	5	6

Number of kids

350

355

360

Several other children in the class arrived at similar solutions, but I thought Andy's way of organizing information was interesting. Many had to struggle to keep track of their numbers. When we shared strategies, the children liked Andy's method as much as I did.

I was hoping that someone would come up with a system of doing these division problems that was similar to the conventional algorithm (that is, the way I learned it and the way I've always taught it before), but I don't think they were ready for that yet.

At this point I am again stuck. How much do I tell? I feel like I can't take extra risks with these kids. What will their teachers say when they go on to middle school? So do I lead them to inventing a new algorithm, or do I teach the old method, or do I leave it as it is? The children seem to understand what they are doing, but the process is long. They are becoming more organized in their thinking and more interested in the methods the other kids are using. One person even asked if everyone could give a report on "their way." I was surprised at how attentive they were when Andy slowly explained his strategy and several of the others followed with theirs. They seemed truly interested. Even when it took the whole math period to go over three strategies, they still wanted to hear more and invent new ways.

The children eagerly took their problems home for homework. "Can we write about our ideas once we figure them out?" someone asked as we left the room together. That sure warmed my heart!

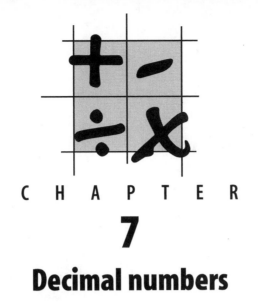

C H A P T E R

7

Decimal numbers

How does the base ten structure of the number system translate across the decimal point? The cases in chapter 7 were chosen to explore this question. As you read the cases, in which the children try to understand decimals, take notes on these points:

■ How do the children employ their understanding of whole numbers, and how do their ideas about place value extend to places smaller than one?

■ What new concepts do they need in order to understand what decimals are and how they function?

Tenths and hundredths

Henrietta

GRADES 6 AND 7 (SPECIAL ED), OCTOBER

I have been thinking about how complicated decimals are for my special-needs students. In my class, we have been working with manipulatives to explore decimal place value and addition of decimals. One boy, Steven, has been having a lot of difficulty. I met with him a couple of days after school this week to review reading, building, and adding decimals.

We begin with .25 + .6. Steven reads this problem to me as 2 tenths and 5 hundredths and 6 tenths. When I prompt him to read the first number again, he is confused. "You mean write it in words?"

I assume he is referring to past math classes in which we read decimals written out in words, and then wrote them as decimal numbers. I ask if he can read .25 as one decimal number. This is a recurring difficulty for Steven. He seems to be able to separate the tenths and hundredths, but not easily read them as one decimal number, 25 hundredths.

Steven now proceeds to build the problem. He pulls out 2 tenth-rods and 5 hundredth-cubes.

Then he counts out 6 hundredth-cubes.

He reports that his answer is 2 tenths and 12 hundredths. I urge him to count again. He puts one hundredth-cube back in the box, and writes out the problem this way:

```
  .25
+ .6
-----
 .211
```

Steven reads his answer: "It's 2 tenths and 11 hundredths." I suggest he look again at the original problem and reread it to me. "Two tenths, 5 hundredths, and 6 tenths. Oh!" Steven removes the 6 hundredth-cubes and replaces them with 6 tenth-rods. The total now looks like this:

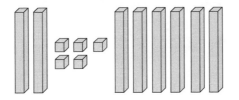

He counts his rods and cubes and says, "It's 8 tenths and 5 hundredths." I write .85 and ask if there is another way to read it as hundredths. Steven is confused again, but finally gets the idea that I want him to assume that his answer is built out of hundredth-cubes. But he doesn't have any idea why. He counts by ones to 80 on the rods, then counts 81 up to 85, and writes:

```
  .25
+ .6
-----
 .85
```

The next day, Steven returns to my room after school and works on the problem .39 + .4. He reads the problem as "3 tenths, 9 hundredths, and 4 tenths," and builds the following:

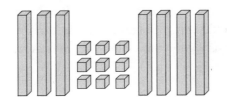

I ask him if he could reread the .39 as if it were built entirely of hundredth-cubes. He counts each unit on a rod by ones up to 30, then by ones from 31 to 39. "Thirty-nine hundredths," he says, and writes:

$$
\begin{array}{r}
.39 \\
+ .4 \\
\hline
.79
\end{array}
$$

"The answer is 7 tenths and 9 hundredths," Steven tells me. For .28 + .37, Steven builds:

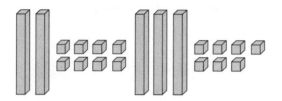

He writes:

$$
\begin{array}{r}
.28 \\
+ .37 \\
\hline
.51
\end{array}
$$

I ask if he can trade in some rods or cubes to show the answer with fewer pieces. He replaces 10 hundredth-cubes with one rod, writes .65, and says, "6 tenths and 5 hundredths."

Again I ask if he can say the number in hundredths. He laboriously starts counting by ones on the rods. "Is there an easier way to count them?" I ask. He suggests counting by twos. We count by twos to 60.

Then he decides to count by tens to 60 and by ones from 61 to 65: "Sixty-five hundredths."

For his final problem, 2.15 + 1.90, Steven attempts to count wholes and hundredths. He lays out 2 whole flats and 15 hundredth-cubes, then 1 flat, and industriously begins counting out hundredth-cubes to 90. I wonder if our working on the 65 hundredths somehow has impressed upon him that he has to build this problem in hundredths, as well as read it as wholes and hundredths. When I ask him if there is an easier way to

40

45

50

55

Building a System of Tens

build the problem, he trades in 10 hundredth-cubes for one tenth-rod, leaving this grouping for 2.15:

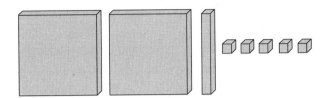

Putting away fistfuls of hundredth-cubes, he builds the following for 1.90: 60

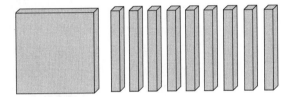

Then he decides to trade again, replacing the 10 rods with 1 whole flat, getting this for the total:

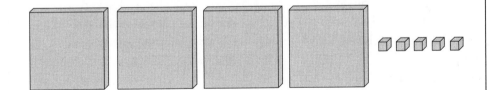

Steven reads his answer as "4 wholes and 5 hundredths." He tells me there are no tenths and writes 4.5 for the answer. After we discuss how to show "no tenths" as a number, he rewrites his answer as 4.05 and reads 65
what he has written as, "4 wholes, no tenths, 5 hundredths."

Steven has many issues about place value and the meaning of number. I wonder about the problem of building with these manipulatives and then translating the physical amount into a single decimal number expressed in the smallest place value. When Steven sees 2 tenth-rods, he 70
doesn't easily see the 20 units within.

Paragraphs, sentences, words . . .

Nicole

GRADE 5, NOVEMBER

When my students were using calculators to figure averages during our study of statistics, they noticed that many answers included a decimal, sometimes a long or repeating one. They were curious about these strange numbers, and I decided to use their interest to begin a study of decimals, a major portion of our fifth-grade curriculum.

We began by looking back at some word problems we had worked on in the first few weeks of school, with a context involving the students' daily silent reading time. This was one of the problems:

 Rob wants to read one hundred pages of his book before his next conference in seven days. How many pages should he read each day?

When the students had worked on the problem in September, some had divided and found the answer to be 14, remainder 2. Today I asked them to look at the problem again, use their calculators, and see what happens. They agreed that their calculators were reporting the answer in this way:

$$100 \div 7 = 14.285714$$

I asked them to think about what these two different answers meant. "What's the remainder 2 that we got the first time?" I asked.

Rob responded, "It means you could read 14 pages each day, and you'd still have 2 pages left to read."

Many other children nodded, and Deyon reemphasized Rob's idea saying, "Yes, it's 2 pages."

Jordy added, "It means you could read 14 pages for 5 days, and then read 15 pages on the other 2 days. Then you would get to 100." I was pleased to see Jordy engaged in a math problem. An avid reader, he frequently tunes out during math.

Andrea leapt in to say, "I tried 14 times 7 and I got 98. That means you would still have 2 pages to read." I wondered if Andrea had been paying attention to what the other students were saying, and if she saw any connection to her own idea. She didn't seem to. Rob, however, nodded as if he understood that she was restating the idea he had suggested in the beginning.

Ted waved his hand in the air eagerly. "I did 14 and 2 tenths times 7 and I got 99 and 4 tenths." He didn't offer an explanation for his discovery. However, I realized that he had opened the door for our discussion to move toward reconsidering decimals.

"Then what is the 'point two eight five seven one four' in the calculator answer we got?" I asked.

Quietly, right by my elbow, Sherika said, "The 2 is like a paragraph." Sherika is a talkative and active learner who usually sees the big picture, both in problem-solving situations and in literature. I wasn't surprised that she had such an interesting idea to offer, and I wanted the class to hear and consider it.

"Explain what you're thinking, Sherika," I invited.

"I think the 2 is like a paragraph," she answered. "It's like you need to read 14 pages each day and another paragraph." My mind was spinning as I thought about what Sherika was saying. I was quite sure she was referring to the 2 tenths when she said, "the 2." It seemed like a very powerful interpretation of a decimal remainder in a division problem. I could clearly see the difference between Sherika's idea, in which she was considering the 2 as a portion of a page to be read each day, and the previous ideas, which had suggested that 14 pages be read each day, with the extra 2 pages being read at some point along the way. I wondered if Sherika really knew what she was suggesting.

I invited the class to pursue her idea. "Who would like to restate what you think Sherika is saying and maybe add to it?"

Jeremy's eyes lit up as he raised his hand to volunteer, "I think I get it. In the 14.285714 it's like the 2 is a paragraph and the 8 is a sentence and the 5 is a word and the 7 is a letter and the 1 is half a letter. I don't know what the 4 is. Only the 14 really counts anyway. The other pieces are really small, especially after you get beyond the sentences."

Like Jordy, Jeremy is an avid reader. He isn't as engaged in math as I would like, though he has flashes of understanding that indicate he could be a powerful problem-solver. It interested me that this particular context—their silent reading time—apparently enabled him to conceptualize something that I believed he was, at best, just barely beginning to understand.

His analysis of the problem also reminded me of a context we had explored a few days earlier. I had asked the students if they would rather have 2 and 5 tenths grams of gold or 2 and 33 hundredths grams of gold. In that context, they had begun to refer to the far right decimal places as unimportant. Jeremy himself had taken to referring to them as "dust." He would say, "The numbers closer to the decimal point mean more. The others are just dust; they don't matter." I wondered if he was connecting that context to this one about pages read, and beginning to formulate a general theory for himself.

"That's pretty interesting, Jeremy," I said. "Does it make sense to you that it could work that way?"

"Well, it doesn't *really* make sense," he answered. "I mean, you don't have pieces of words to be read and things like that. It does make sense in some ways though; like how I said, it's really only the first few numbers that make a difference. The rest are too small to matter."

"Did Sherika's idea get you thinking this way?" I asked, musing to myself how often Jeremy lacked sensitivity and appreciation for his classmates.

"Yes!" he responded enthusiastically.

I was pleased that several students had connected their ideas during this lesson, and that we had considered a context that appeared to have significance for many of them. It was exciting that Jeremy, whose ideas in math sometimes lacked connection or relevance to mathematics as a discipline, was able to extend an idea beyond the immediate context to a point at which it still made sense mathematically, even though it didn't make sense in the given context. I began searching for another context that would offer such a fruitful way to consider decimals. I knew I would need a situation, like the reading problems, in which an answer could be interpreted both as a remainder of discrete items and as a decimal with portions of items.

It seemed that we were on our way toward building an understanding of decimals as parts of wholes. I thought we would return to this problem, and to the interpretations offered us by Sherika and Jeremy, as we pursued our investigations.

Why do we need rules?

Nicole

Over the past few years I have come to believe that it is important for my fifth-grade students to be able to articulate and communicate their understanding of math concepts and solutions for problems. I often give "rule writing" a context by asking how we would communicate what we know about something to someone by telephone, or to a new student who had just entered our class. We regularly engage in such dialogue in class, and I have assumed they understand that being able to communicate ideas in words is an important part of understanding mathematics. A recent class made me rethink that assumption.

One day in January, in our continuing investigation of decimals, I gave each group of four students a pair of numbers similar to these:

We had been studying decimals for some time, and the class seemed to have a pretty good understanding of how to compare the relative size of two decimal numbers. I asked them to decide which of the two numbers was larger and be ready to present their ideas to the class. Almost every group completed the task quickly, with ease, and correctly.

We posted the number pairs on the board. Next to them I hung "rules" we had written previously for whole numbers. Those rules stated the following:

1. The number that has more digits is larger.

2. If both numbers have the same number of digits or columns, start comparing from the left. The first one that has a higher digit is higher.

I challenged the class to think by saying, "It seemed to be pretty easy for you to decide which of the two numbers was larger. I'm wondering if you used rules to figure it out. Would the rules for decimals be the same as the rules we made for whole numbers?" I asked them to reflect individually, in their notebooks. I suggested it might help to try to think of two decimal numbers that followed the whole-number rules and two that didn't. After a few minutes of quiet thinking and writing, I invited them to share what they had come up with.

Alison tried first. "I know I understand it," she said, "and I think I can say it. First you look at the tenths and hundredths and thousandths and . . . and . . . ." She smiled in frustration that the thoughts in her head were not coming out as clearly as she had hoped.

Casey tried next. "You look at the tenths because they're biggest. It's different than our rules from before. The tenths are biggest."

Luke's hand shot up. "Yeah, I agree with Casey. You look at the tenths. But I don't really know a rule. This is hard."

Javier insisted on talking next. In his usual dramatic way, he rose front and center and used his hands for emphasis. "See, it's like this," he said. "Either one is bigger or the other is bigger or they're equal, and that's it!" Javier seemed almost to be joking about how obvious his statement was. However, it had real mathematical validity.

I responded, "You know, Javier, what you just said is the way mathematicians talk about things. I heard you say that there are only three choices: Either one is bigger, or the other is, or they're equal, right?" Javier grinned in response.

Picking up Javier's idea, J.R. said insistently, "Here's what you know. You assume one of them is bigger. You start with the realization that one must be bigger, so that's that." At this point I sensed that the students were almost backtracking, as if they were trying to find solid ground on which to base their rules. Even though they had devised rules for whole numbers, and operated as if they knew rules for decimals, they didn't seem to be able to go straight to formulating rules. There was frustration in the air, and soon it would erupt.

First we heard from Kelly. She seemed to be referring back to Alison's idea. "I think you look at the whole numbers first because they are biggest. Then you look at tenths and hundredths and thousandths."

Quiet, thoughtful Carlos raised his hand and added, "I agree. You start with the tenths and then go to hundredths."

I asked again, "So what is the rule? Can you say the rule?"

J.R., taking a leadership role uncharacteristic for him in math class, spoke with some exasperation, "I *can't* explain it. Anyway, we don't need a rule because we get it already. It's too hard to say a rule. What's it for anyway? We understand it because we can do it."

Backing him up, Luke—who often delights in reciting rules, even when he doesn't understand them—said, "Yeah. Why do we need a rule? We get it already because we can do it. When you really understand something you don't need a rule for it." I sensed that these two were reflecting sentiments widely held in class at that moment. I thought hard about what they were saying. The positive side of it was that they were emphasizing understanding and saying that when you really understand, you don't need a rule to tell you what to do. The negative side haunted me as I wondered whether they really *did* understand, since they couldn't state a rule for how they were operating, especially given the support of many students working together.

I puzzled through my own confusion by restating what I thought I had heard. "So you're saying that when you really understand something, you don't need a rule for it. That the rule is extra and too much work and you don't need it because you do understand and you know you do." Many children nodded. I realized the irony of their argument. In another setting these students would have been expected to learn rules put forth by their teacher and use them to operate. If they had questioned the rules, the teacher might have said, "You don't need to understand. It's the rule." Now they were insisting that they didn't need rules precisely because they *did* understand.

Later, when I looked over their notebooks, I found evidence that many had been thinking hard and experiencing a good bit of confusion as they worked individually. Many stated clearly that the whole-number rules wouldn't always work. Some gave examples of number pairs in which they worked and others in which they didn't. No one ventured a decimal rule.

I knew I didn't agree with them that rules are irrelevant. I could tell that the thinking we had done together was challenging and confusing to all of us. I realized that something about the word "rule" was irritating to them. I suspected that their own "rules" for comparing whole numbers were not entirely clear to them. Clearly, their concepts of place value were still not solid. I left the topic for that day, but I knew we would return to it often.

Chapter 7

When the answer *is* important

Nicole

GRADE 5, MARCH

In the middle of March, my class returned to the study of decimals after a break of several weeks. I offered a problem that, I hoped, would force them to consider how they could correctly add decimals, including tenths, hundredths, and thousandths.

"Pretend you are a jeweler," I said. "Sometimes people come in to get rings resized. When you cut down a ring to make it smaller, you keep the small portion of gold in exchange for the work you have done. Recently you have collected these amounts." I wrote on the board:

1.14 g   .089 g   .3 g

"Now you have a repair job to do for which you need some gold. You are wondering if you have enough. Work together with your group to figure out how much gold you have collected. Be prepared to show the class your solution."

I circulated around the room overhearing conversations and thinking about what my students were considering. Nikki said tentatively, "We could line the numbers up on the right like you do with other numbers."

Ned disagreed, suggesting instead, "Maybe we should line up the decimals, but I don't know why we would do that."

"I think you're suggesting that you might line this problem up differently from the way you line up whole-number addition. Is that right?" I asked. Ned nodded, and I continued, "Why do you line whole numbers up the way you do? What's the reason for it?"

"I don't know," Ned answered. "It's just the way you do it. That's how we learned to do it."

Malik offered, "I think it would help if we drew a picture, like of the blocks. Maybe we could figure it out then."

In the next group, Rob, assertive, cooperative, and self-confident, said, "I'm sure we should line them up in sections." His groupmates listened,

275

280

285

290

295

300

but didn't seem to understand what he was suggesting until he added, "You need to put tenths with tenths and hundredths with hundredths."

In the back corner, Johanna, Jerry, and Jaron had already set up their problem as shown in Figure 3.

"What happened to the decimal numbers?" I asked them.

Jaron replied, confidently, "We just decided to drop the decimals and add the numbers like usual. That way we could line them up on the right and add. We left the zero in there, but you can just leave it out since it doesn't mean anything."

"Do you all agree?" I probed.

"Yes," the other two responded, smiling.

"Are you saying, then, that if you start out with 1 and 14 hundredths grams of gold and some other little bits that it adds up to 206 grams of gold?" I continued.

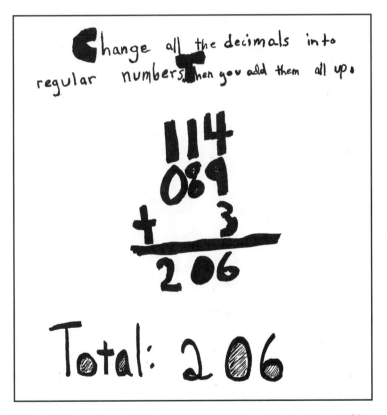

Figure 3 Johanna, Jerry, and Jaron decide to simplify the problem by getting rid of the decimal points.

Nicole

They seemed a bit puzzled, and looked again at their work, but I was called away to another group.

We had time for only a short discussion before lunch, and the debate centered around whether the correct answer was 1.529 or 2.06. Rob quickly demonstrated his group's solution, as shown in Figure 4.

Ned asked, "How did you decide to line the numbers up like that?" Ned is such a strong mathematical thinker that it didn't surprise me that he was still searching for a reason to line up the numbers in the way he had intuitively guessed was correct. Perhaps he was hoping that Rob would give him the explanation he hadn't been able to formulate.

320

325

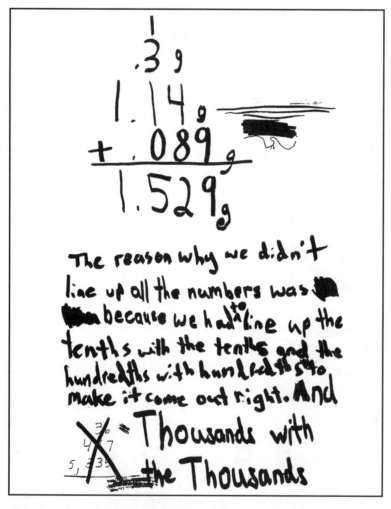

Figure 4 Rob's group aligns the three decimal numbers by place value.

Building a System of Tens

Rob responded, "The reason we did it this way was we thought we needed to line up the tenths with the tenths and the hundredths with the hundredths to make it come out right. You also need to line up the thousandths with the thousandths." That was a more mathematically precise explanation than Rob had offered his group when he had said, "You need to line up the sections." 330

Nikki wasn't satisfied. She listened and wondered, "I see what you did and why you did it, but our group tried something different, and we got a different answer. Do you think there could be two right answers?" She wasn't truly surprised when he answered, "No. I think there is only one right answer." 335

Jaron then entered the debate, saying adamantly, "I think your answer is way too big. Our group just dropped the decimals and added. You can also drop the zero since it doesn't stand for anything. We got 2 and 6 hundredths for an answer, and I think that's right." 340

Teresa, always searching for sense, burst into the discussion with, "What do you mean their answer is too big? Your answer is even bigger!" It was clear at this point that for many students, the motivation to continue the discussion was the search for the right answer. Since the problem had a context and our imaginary jeweler would want to know precisely how many grams she had, any old answer wasn't satisfying them. 345

Teresa continued with, "Anyway, you can't just drop that zero. It has to be there or you get 89 hundredths instead of 89 thousandths, and they're not the same at all." I knew figuring out this zero question was important, but I decided to sidestep it for now and return to it another time. 350

I turned and asked Malik to share his idea of how to arrive at a solution. His group had not written anything down, but they had had a very thoughtful exchange, and they were all actively involved in the discussion. He said, "Well, I was thinking it would help if we could draw a picture, like of the blocks. I tried to do it, but I couldn't quite figure it out. If I had the flats be one whole, then the rods are tenths and the units are hundredths, but I don't know how to draw the thousandths except as dots. Then I can't really tell what's going on." 355 360

Jaron insisted, "I still say you can drop the zero because it's just nothing."

On the way to lunch, Ben stopped by my desk to say, "I think I know how we could draw a picture. If we use the thousand block to be one whole then we can use the flats for tenths, the rods for hundredths, and we have the units for thousandths."

"Do you think you could do the problem with the blocks then?" I asked him.

"I'm sure I could," he answered.

That afternoon, during quiet reading time, I asked Ben if he wanted to invite Rob and Kwame to work in the hall with him to see if they could demonstrate the problem in the way he had suggested with the blocks. I thought if Ben could explain it to them, then maybe the three of them could explain their understanding to the class.

The next day the three boys set up their demonstration. I told the class that Ben had come up with a way to use the blocks to include thousandths, and that I thought it might help us pursue the idea that Malik had proposed, that he could understand it if he could draw it. They each took a part in explaining what they had done. Their demonstration with base ten blocks looked like this:

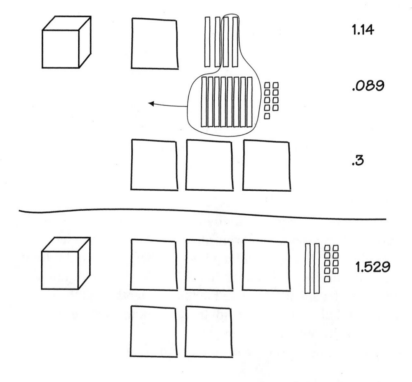

Malik was riveted to the show, listening carefully and nodding. Teresa also seemed to connect to the explanation, especially realizing that the zero was very significant in deciding which blocks to use. After everyone had a chance to observe and ask questions, I asked students to write in their journals what they thought were the correct procedure and answer, and what had helped them most to understand. Many students mentioned that the demonstration had made it clear to them that you needed to add tenths to tenths and hundredths to hundredths or you wouldn't get the "right" answer.

I invited them to continue thinking about adding decimals by devising problems of their own. The next day, Andrea and Ned showed up with pages covered with carefully done problems, like the ones in Figure 5.

385

390

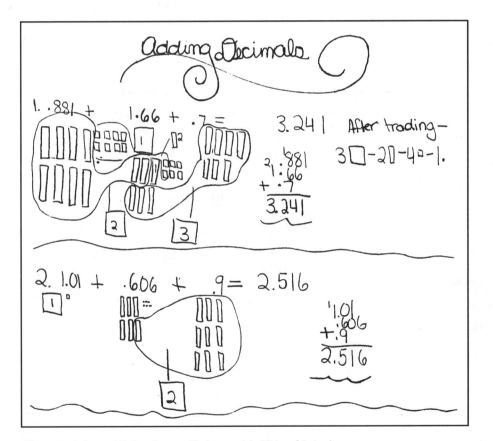

Figure 5 Andrea and Ned use base ten blocks to model addition of decimals.

It seemed that, in this instance, my students' determined search for a right answer had led them to a much deeper understanding of place value, decimals, and addition with decimals of varying places. I was delighted that they cared so much about getting the "right" answer.

C A S E   29

Quotients as decimals

Tara

GRADE 6, FEBRUARY

For homework, I asked my sixth-grade students to write decimal word problems. The next day in class, the students sat in groups of three and exchanged problems to work through and discuss. The following is a description of what happened in one group. It started with this problem:

? Mrs. Leonard went to Pinches and Pounds and bought 4.0 pounds of gumballs. She shared them with Ms. Field and Mr. McCoy. If each of them got the same amount of gumballs, how much did they each get? Were there any left over?

Nanette divided 4.0 by 3 like this:

$$3 \overline{)4.0}^{1.33}$$

In the beginning of our decimal explorations, I encouraged students to explain their thinking using base ten blocks. We called them decimal squares, letting the flat equal 1 whole, the rod equal 1 tenth, and the unit equal 1 hundredth.

Building a System of Tens

Using the decimal blocks, Charlene explained what she had done. She represented the four pounds this way:

The last decimal block, 1 whole pound, is split into tenths.

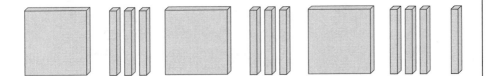

"Then take the 1 tenth left over and split that into hundredths. It's supposed to be 1.33 with a remainder of 1," explained Charlene.

415

Nanette responded, "That's what I got this time when I did the problem. Before, I got 1.3 with a remainder of 1."

```
      1.3
  3 ) 4.0
      3
      1 0
        9
        1
```

One of the girls used the calculator and got 1.3333333. Nanette's eyes got big!

420

An-mei volunteered, "I think it depends on the zeros that you put on the end of the number you are dividing."

Charlene continued, "Like this is 1.3," and wrote:

$$3 \overline{)4.0} = 1.3$$

Nanette then suggested, "Put another zero on the end of the number and you get 1.33, and another zero gives us 1.333."

$$3 \overline{)4.00} = 1.33 \qquad 3 \overline{)4.000} = 1.333$$

Following my instructions, this group decided to go on to the next problem, putting this exploration aside for the time being. However, as An-mei and Nanette pursued the problem I had given them, Charlene went back to the questions that had been inspired by the first problem. A few minutes later, she had drawn An-mei and Nanette back in, saying, "What I found out is that these are the numbers that repeat—3, 6, and 9— when you use them to divide. And that the repeated number is the number after the decimal point."

Charlene wrote the following to show what she meant:

$$3 \overline{)4.000} = 1.333 \qquad 6 \overline{)4.000} = .666 \qquad 9 \overline{)4.000} = .444$$

An-mei responded, "I think it only happens when you divide, not multiply."

After more experimenting with the calculator, Charlene said, "Look! Eight doesn't work."

$$8 \overline{)3.000} = .375 \qquad 8 \overline{)6.00} = .75 \qquad 8 \overline{)9.000} = 1.125$$

The group went to work dividing by other even numbers. Initially, they thought that the even numbers did not produce repeating numbers or run-ons, as they called them. Nanette did a few different examples:

$$2 \overline{)4.00} = 2.00 \qquad 4 \overline{)9.00} = 2.25 \qquad 6 \overline{)3.0} = .5$$

Then she proposed another theory, and tried it out: "Nine works most of the time, but not always, I think."

$$9 \overline{)2.000} = .222 \qquad 9 \overline{)4.000} = .444 \qquad 9 \overline{)8.000} = .888 \qquad 9 \overline{)5.000} = .555 \qquad 9 \overline{)7.000} = .777 \qquad 9 \overline{)6.000} = .666$$

Charlene then added to the theory: "It might work with 3, 6, or 9 as the dividend, but only if the numbers are not the divisor. I think that the numbers only work some of the time because they are divisible by 9."

I am not sure I know what Charlene meant. I think she may have begun to notice something important, but the 42-minute class had come to an end without any resolution of the issue of repeating decimals. The rest of the class had pursued a different task altogether, but the work of these three girls really intrigued me. I wanted them to know that I valued their work, and I wanted them to share what they had done with the class.

About a week later, I asked An-mei, Nanette, and Charlene to explain to the whole class what they had discovered. Each person in the class was given a calculator, and the three girls went to the board and explained about repeating decimals. The class had time to ask questions of this group and help figure out which numbers would make repeating decimals. This gave all of us, including me, the chance to catch up to the work that An-mei, Nanette, and Charlene had done.

I know we are not finished. I was unsure how to proceed, but when I watched these three girls take over the math class, it was one of those "teaching moments" that happens every now and then. The class was impressed with their discovery. I was pretty amazed, too!

C H A P T E R

8

Highlights of related research

by Sophia Cohen

Up to now, *Building a System of Tens* has focused on case materials written by teachers in K–6 classrooms. Through these cases, we have been able to look very closely at some of the complexities facing children as they build a conception of the base ten structure of our number system. In chapter 8, we shift our focus in two ways. First, we now look at the story emerging from research on the development of these understandings, and at the connections between this research-based story and the classroom cases in the previous seven chapters. The case writers and the researchers share an important interest: carefully observing and coming to a better understanding of children's mathematical thinking. We bring together the research and the cases because both provide windows on the development of very complex ideas among children. The second shift in focus that we make here is from the particular to the general. Our picture is less fine-grained now, and we take this step back from the individual idea, or child, or classroom, to view a broader picture of the whole set of issues children confront and work through as they come to understand the system-of-tens structure of our number system.

This essay examines five different themes, drawing on relevant mathematics, research, and cases from *Building a System of Tens.* First we consider the spoken and written systems for representing number, their similarities and differences, and the difficulties children face in learning about the written system. Second, we examine what is involved in understanding that a group of any size can itself be counted as a "one"; that, for instance, ten is simultaneously 1 ten and 10 ones. Third, we examine the issues that arise for children as they add and subtract multidigit numbers; fourth, we focus on issues related to multiplication and division. Finally, we take up decimal fractions and explore the ways children work to build understandings of these numbers, starting from their understandings of whole numbers and of common fractions. Together these five themes illustrate the issues children confront as they build more and more powerful understandings of the base ten number system.

S E C T I O N **1**

Written number vs. spoken number

Spoken and written number are different systems. They are related to each other in complex ways; building an understanding of each system and its relationship to the other involves a substantial amount of work.

While we are all aware of both speaking and writing number, we do not often stop to consider the ways in which spoken and written number are similar to, or different from, one another. As it turns out, in English, the relationships are rather complicated. Children come to school relatively experienced with the spoken system and relatively inexperienced with the written system and with the similarities or differences between them. The spoken and written number systems have two very important similarities. First, both systems use successive powers of ten as the units. In other words, in both spoken and written number, we work with units of ones, tens, hundreds, thousands, and so forth. Second, both systems use ten different words or marks to represent the numbers 0 through 9, and then reuse these same words or marks to indicate how many of the larger units there are.

These similarities are so impressive that the differences may, at first, be difficult for adults to notice. But the differences are also impressive. The primary difference is that in the number system of spoken English, we explicitly name the value of the units (e.g., four *thousand* five *hundred eighty* three), whereas in the written system, we rely on unnamed position, or place value, to convey their value (e.g., 4,583).

An experiment can illustrate the significance of this. Imagine that you write the words for a four-digit number on separate cards. On one card you write *four thousand,* on the next *five hundred,* on the next *eighty,* and on the last *three.* Now scramble and read these cards; *three five hundred four thousand eighty* is one possibility. Even scrambled, the number words still indicate the original quantity. They don't do it in the conventional way, but they are not ambiguous, nor has their meaning changed. Now imagine that instead of writing number words on these cards, you write the numerals for the same quantity. On the first card you write 4, on the next 5, on the next 8, and on the last 3. Now, when you scramble these, what happens? Or what if you maintain the order, but separate the numerals from one another? Your representation no longer maintains the original meaning. The meaning of the unit size in written number is conveyed only through the place or position in which the number is written. The unit value is not otherwise explicitly marked or named, as it is in the spoken system.

The learner's job is even more difficult because, in English, the spoken number system is irregular in many ways and does not consistently highlight the base ten structure of our number system. For example:

- English number words for two-digit numbers do not include the word *ten.* Instead we use *-teen* and *-ty.* Thus, not only do we not use the word *ten* itself, but we use two different variants of it.

- The placement of the ten in *-teen* words is the reverse of the placement of the ten in *-ty* words. So while we say "four*teen*," indicating first how many ones and then how many tens, we say "for*ty*-four," indicating first how many tens and then how many ones.

- The words *eleven* and *twelve* don't mark tens at all.

- The words *thirteen* and *fifteen* do mark tens and ones, but alter the pronunciation of the three and five, making the *-teen* pattern (thirteen through nineteen) difficult to notice and use.

- A similar problem exists with the *-ty* words: *twenty, thirty,* and *fifty* alter the pronunciation of the *two, three,* and *five* on which they are based.

Further, when speaking of numbers written with four digits, we sometimes say *eleven hundred* or *twenty-five hundred* rather than *one thousand one hundred* or *two thousand five hundred,* breaking with the strict tens structure.

Karen Fuson (1990) found that, because of the differences between the spoken and written systems, three issues arise for children as they begin to map between spoken and written number. The cases in this casebook provide examples that parallel Fuson's findings.

The first issue emerges because in spoken number, we can omit a value term as we name some quantities, and still be clear on the quantity; this is not paralleled in written number. In other words, we can say "six hundred two," but its written equivalent is not 62; in the written system, where position or place marks unit size, we must write 602. We do not say "six hundred, zero tens, two" (although we can imagine such a system), presumably because the values of the units are named in the spoken system, and the "zero tens" isn't necessary.

In Muriel's case 14, second graders are thinking about questions related to this issue: what zero represents, and whether or not it represents the same thing in the numbers 07 and 70. These children seem to be thinking very seriously about the structure of our written number system, and are beginning to grapple with the question of how and why zero of a given unit (ones, tens, hundreds) is represented.

A second difficulty that arises from the differences between spoken and written number could be viewed as the reverse of the first. The question here is whether each system tolerates more than nine of a given unit. For example, a child who is adding 58 and 37 might come to an answer of "eighty-fifteen" and get stuck at this point. In the spoken system, "eighty-fifteen" is a sensible, if not conventional, representation of the quantity that results from adding 58 and 37. However, 815 is not the corresponding written number; nor is there a way to write that number without symbols representing the implied operation of addition (80 + 15).

In Dawn's case 11, kindergartners are discussing how to write the number that follows 59. They debate whether it should be 510 (5 and 10) or 60. These children are working on, among other things, questions like those involved in the "eighty-fifteen" example. They are uncovering elements of the structure of our written number system.

A third difficulty stems from the fact that spoken number names the unit while written number does not. In spoken number, the values are concatenated; that is, they follow one another, so we say "one hundred thirty-two." Written numbers, on the other hand, are embedded in one another; for the spoken "one hundred thirty-two," we write 132. It is not conventional to write 100302 for this quantity, although we see many children inventing this notation (Behr, 1976; Bell & Burns, 1981).

In the cases in chapters 2 and 3, we see children struggling with this issue, both in questions of how to write numbers and how to interpret them. In Danielle's case 15, children wonder whether *one hundred ninety-five* is written 195 or 1095 or 10095; in Muriel's case 14, a second grader argues that *one hundred twenty-five* cannot be correctly written as 100205. In Beverly's case 7 and Donna's case 12, the children have not yet unpacked the embedded numbers in the written form. For instance, we see a first grader in case 7 struggling to figure out that 120 is 12 tens, and that 210 is 21 tens. Donna's second-grade students are just coming to see that 38 is comprised of 3 tens and 8 ones. The written number 132 can be understood as 1 hundred + 3 tens + 2 ones; but it can also be seen as 13 tens + 2 ones, or as 132 ones, or as 1 hundred + 32 ones. As the cases make clear, these equivalencies are not at all trivial or obvious.

Children are faced with an enormous amount of work to sort through the ways we write and speak about number. Beyond this, of course, we want children to connect these symbols to some sense of the quantities they represent. We turn to these issues next.

Seeing a ten as "one"

Being able to label the tens place and the ones place, or even being able to count by tens, does not necessarily signal an understanding that 1 ten is simultaneously 10 ones. Becoming mindful of this relationship between tens and ones, or staying mindful of it, is neither simple nor trivial.

Mommy, if you are 40, then 30 years ago you had to be 1. Oh, wait! I was forgetting about 31, 32, 33, 34, . . .

— Second grader (October)

In this short quote, we see one moment of a child's struggle to keep track of a ten as both 1 ten and 10 ones. We see a very similar struggle played out in Lucy's case 6, in which third grader Sarah is confused about how many black cubes (representing ones) to move over to the yellows (representing tens): If she is representing the number 10, should she move ten cubes or should she move one? These children are showing us how far from obvious is the ten-for-one trade structure in our number system. While children may fairly readily come to label the leftmost digit of a two-digit number as the *tens* and the rightmost digit as the *ones,* this does not necessarily signal an understanding of the "ten" as being 10 ones and thereby related to the ones in a quantitative way. When children first shift their focus from counting the 10 ones that are necessary for making ten to the group of ten itself, they lose sight of the ones structure inside the ten. To simultaneously consider ten as 1 ten and as 10 ones is extremely difficult. Both our cases and more formal research suggest that working out this aspect of number is a protracted process (Beishuizen, 1993; Cobb, 1995; Cobb & Wheatley, 1988; Fuson, 1990; Steffe, 1988; Steffe, Cobb, & Von Glasersfeld, 1988). One study will be reviewed in depth here, but much other work has also been done on this topic.

An experiment conducted by Sharon Ross (1989) clearly exposes children's initial understandings of two-digit number as based on units of a value of "one," and children's difficulty in imposing a tens structure on these same quantities. Ross interviewed 60 children, all of whom were students in grades 2 through 5. She posed several problems to each child. We will look at just three of the problems that illustrate the pattern of Ross's findings.

Ross gave children a bag of sticks and asked them to spill the sticks out and tell her how many sticks there were. Nearly all the children were able to count the sticks correctly and to tell her that there were 25 sticks. They were also able to write that number correctly. Next, Ross circled the 5 in the 25 that a child had written and asked, "Does this part of your 25 have anything to do with how many sticks you have?" She asked the same question about the 2 in 25. Only 26 of the 60 children correctly explained the meanings of the 2 and the 5 in this written number. The remaining children said that the individual digits either had nothing to do with the number of sticks, or that the 2 was for 2 of them and the 5 was for 5 of them, or they invented meanings such as "5 is for half of ten," or "2 means count by twos."

The second problem that Ross asked children to think about involved the relationship between the digits in the written number 52 and that same quantity represented by base ten blocks in a standard tens and ones partitioning: 5 tens rods and 2 unit cubes. Ross asked, for example, if the 2 had anything to do with how many base ten blocks were on the table. With these questions, 44 of the same 60 students answered correctly.

The third problem that Ross posed was the same as the second in every way except that now the base ten blocks representing 52 were 4 tens rods and 12 unit cubes. When asked about the meanings of 5 and 2 in this context, only 20 of these 60 children answered correctly, indicating that this problem was no easier for the children than the original sticks problem that provided no orderly groupings.

What accounts for the difference in the number of correct responses when the arrangement of tens and ones matches the digits in the written number? Why were so many more children answering this problem correctly?

A follow-up study of 30 third graders helps to clarify what is going on here. Ross wondered if the children's success on the questions relating to the standard partitioning with the base ten blocks had nothing to do with a child's sense of the relationship between tens and ones in these materials (or anywhere). She wondered if it was simply that the children could identify 5 of one kind of block and 2 of another. If the children were just searching for referents for these digits, then these correct answers were deceptive. She now set up a situation in which a child who was just searching for a referent would answer differently from a child who understood the relationship between tens and ones, and the way that we express this relationship in our written system.

Ross showed children a group of 26 objects, asked them to count the objects, to write down how many they counted, and then to arrange the objects in groups of 4. This arrangement yielded 6 groups of 4 objects each with 2 left over. Now, to Ross's questions about the meaning of the digits in the written number, nearly half of these children responded that the 2 indicates the 2 left over, and the 6 indicates the 6 groups of 4.

Surely Ross's base-ten-block and 6-groups-of-4 problems create contexts that make it relatively easy for children to base their answers on the arrangements of objects to which so much attention has been drawn. Because of this, only children who are very sure of the meanings of the individual digits in a two-digit numeral will answer correctly when the context doesn't suggest it, as it does for the 5-tens-and-2-ones problem. Ross's problems can in some ways be seen as tricks or lures to entice children into basing their answer on something other than the tens-and-ones structure of the quantity, and in this sense they are difficult versions of these questions. But they expose (a) how common it is for elementary school children not to be sure, and (b) how carefully we must examine children's use of structured materials, such as base ten blocks, if we are to understand the child's conceptions.[1]

We have been looking at children's understandings of what, for example, a 2 in the tens place might mean, and what we can conclude based on children's correct answers to routine questions about how many tens and how many ones. There is ample evidence that even when children are able to talk about a tens place and a ones place, and are able to say that 2 is in the tens place, they might not be thinking of ten as both a countable unit and a unit that is itself composed of 10 ones. But what if

---

[1] See also Cobb (1995) for a similar discussion of hundreds boards. He claims that while this is a useful tool for reflection for children who have constructed some sense of ten as itself countable and as composed of 10 ones, he did not observe use of the hundreds board as the source of this understanding.

a child is able to do quite a bit more than just say that this is the tens place and this is the ones place? Or that 25 has 2 tens and 5 ones? What about children who can, for instance, count by tens and ones? What is a correctly applied count of "10, 20, 30, 40, 41, 42, 43 . . ." evidence of? What is "7, 17, 27, 28, 29 . . ." evidence of? Do either of these depend on an understanding that ten is simultaneously 1 ten and 10 ones? The evidence is that these patterns, even in mid-decade, are learnable auditory patterns and can be carried out by a child who counts base ten blocks, or similarly structured materials, while seeing the tens and ones as simply two different kinds of things, like apples and oranges. These counts alone are not necessarily evidence that a child has really understood the quantitative relationship that 1 ten has the same value as 10 ones (Cobb, 1995; Cobb & Wheatley, 1988).

While there is wide agreement among researchers that building a concept of ten as both 1 ten and 10 ones is difficult for children, researchers differ in their descriptions of the conceptions of ten that children build along the way (Steffe et al., 1988; Cobb & Wheatley, 1988; Fuson, 1990, 1992).

S E C T I O N   3

Invented procedures for adding and subtracting

As children gain facility in breaking apart and recombining numbers, they often invent multidigit addition and subtraction procedures. These can be the starting places for deeper understanding of the tens structure itself and how it behaves in computation.

It is an enormous leap from operating with units of one to multidigit computational procedures that use units of tens, hundreds, thousands, and so forth, as well as units of one. To work with units of different values, we must sort out the complicated ways that each is related to the others. The number 107, for example, can be thought of as 1 hundred +

0 tens + 7 ones, or as 10 tens + 7 ones, or as 107 ones; and if we now want to add 38, which is to say 3 tens + 8 ones or 38 ones, to our initial 107, there are several possibilities. We might think about this problem entirely in terms of ones (as we usually would for a problem such as 4 + 2). We could add 107 ones to 38 ones, yielding 145 ones, an answer we could arrive at by counting. Alternatively, we might think about the numbers involved in this problem as each being composed of a certain number of units of different values. Perhaps we set aside the 1 hundred of 107, and then add on 3 tens of 38, and next the 8 ones and the 7 ones. Or, we might think of the 100 as 10 tens, add these to the 3 tens from 38 to find 13 tens, to which we would still need to add the 8 ones and the 7 ones in some way. When it comes to the 7 + 8 portion of this problem, there are also many possibilities. We might add 7 ones to the 8 ones as a single quantity that yields 15 ones, or in parts, for instance, taking 2 ones to add to the 8 ones, thus making a fourteenth ten and 5 more ones.

Any solution that makes use of units other than one either requires some knowledge of the effects of adding units of different values, or it requires a method for modeling and investigating these. In order to combine the 13 tens and 15 ones from our example, and to name this number in a conventional way, a person needs to know the precise quantitative relationships between ones and tens and between tens and hundreds. Similar knowledge is necessary for a multiunit solution to a subtraction problem such as 107 − 38 (although, as we will see later, the subtraction situation poses further difficulties).

Because of the issues that arise during computation, many researchers argue that multidigit addition and subtraction can be a vehicle for learning about the meanings underlying our place value system. They argue that the understanding needn't be thought of as a prerequisite for these computations (Carpenter et al., 1996; Cobb, 1995; Cobb & Wheatley, 1988; Fuson, 1990; Ross, 1989; Wood, 1996), but rather that knowledge of the tens structure grows out of in-depth exploration of computation strategies.

Without explicit instruction, children devise computational procedures that directly model the actions and relations of a word problem. To develop these procedures, children draw on their understanding of counting and of the kinds of change (adding some or taking some away) that affect quantity, that is, their knowledge about making more or making less (Carpenter et al., 1996; Resnick, 1992; Resnick, Lesgold, & Bill, 1990; Madell, 1985). Initially, children's strategies are based in a system of ones (counting all, counting on, and counting back). Eventually, children develop strategies for other-sized groups, including the very powerful use of ones, tens, hundreds, and so forth.

Lynn's case 16 provides examples of both ones-based and tens-based strategies. She describes second graders solving a word problem in which teachers at recess see 38 children around the climbing structure and 25 children playing freeze tag. The problem asks how many children the teachers see. Several children counted by ones to solve this problem. Two children did as follows: They made two Unifix cube collections, one of 38 and one of 25, counting out the cubes one by one. Next, they counted both sets together, starting at one, until all cubes were counted. This contrasts with the solutions of several other children in the same class who worked more abstractly with number and made use of groups of ten, generating solutions such as this one: $30 + 20 = 50$, $8 + 5 = 13$, $50 + 13 = 63$. Like many children, these chose to operate with the larger numbers (in this case, tens) first (Madell, 1985; Kamii, 1989; Kamii, Lewis, & Livingston, 1993).

While this latter-style solution certainly demonstrates some ability to decompose and recombine numbers using groups of tens and ones, we are not able to tell from this example whether any of these children understand $30 + 20 = 50$ to be equivalent to 3 tens + 2 tens = 5 tens, and therefore to be both similar to, and different from, 3 ones + 2 ones = 5 ones. Certainly the children solving this problem by counting out cubes one by one are not looking at the numbers this way.

As numbers get larger, we often (though not always) work with number per se, as opposed to a concrete representation of a number of something. Thus, we can work with 3 tens rather than 3 packages of 10 cookies. Yet, children who are working on understanding the relationships between tens and ones are first able to work with ten as 10 ones only in the presence of some physical model. A more abstract sense of ten as a unit, the ability to manipulate tens as numerals, comes later (Carpenter et al., 1996; Cobb and Wheatley, 1988; Resnick, 1992; Steffe et al., 1988).

Thomas Carpenter, Elizabeth Fennema, and Megan Franke are among the researchers who have described this developmental pattern. Their work is based on careful observation of children solving addition and subtraction problems. In one paper (1996), they provide the following

270

275

280

285

290

295

300

example from a third-grade class that has been asked to solve a word problem involving the sum 54 + 48:

Ms. G: Now everyone go over to Ellen's desk.

ELLEN: They don't need to go to my desk, I can tell them right here.

Ms. G: But I want them to go to your desk; I want them to see exactly what you showed me, and then you can tell me how you could do it without us having to go to your desk.

[The children move around Ellen's desk.]

ELLEN: *[Makes 54 and 48 with tens and ones blocks (5 tens blocks and 4 ones blocks and separately 4 tens blocks and 8 ones blocks)].* I know this was 54, so I went 64, 74, 84, 94 *[Ellen moves one ten block for each count. Then she counts the single cubes, moving a cube with each count.]* 95, 96, . . . 102 . . .

Ms. G: OK, now you told me that you could do this without us moving to your desk. How would you have done that?

ELLEN: OK, I just put 54 in my head, and then I go 48 more. I go 54 *[slight pause]*, 64, 74, 84, 94 *[She puts up a finger with each count to keep track of the tens. At this point she has 4 fingers up. She puts down her fingers and puts them up again with each count as she continues counting by ones.]* 95, 96, 97, . . . 102. (pp. 3–4)

Ellen first solved this problem with blocks. She began with the physical materials to support her count of "64, 74, 84, 94, 95, 96, 97, . . . 102." However, once given the opportunity to share her solution, she was eager to speak about it without blocks, and seemed to have already moved to an understanding that she could communicate without directly manipulating physical objects.

From many examples similar to this sequence with Ellen, Carpenter et al. (1996) propose that

> the manipulations of the blocks become objects of reflection. At some point the numbers involved in counting the blocks also become objects of reflection so that students can operate on the numbers independently of the blocks. A key factor in this process is the continuing discussion of alternative strategies. Students regularly are called upon to articulate

their solutions, to describe in words what they have done with the blocks. In order to be able to describe their strategies, they need to reflect upon them, to decide how to report them verbally. Initially the descriptions are of procedures that have already been carried out. Eventually the words that students use to describe their manipulations of blocks become the solutions themselves. Thus, the verbal description of modeling strategies provides a basis for connecting manipulations of tens blocks and invented algorithms using numbers only. The students do not imitate a strategy that they do not understand; they abstract the physical modeling procedures when they are comfortable doing so. (pp. 12–13)

Carpenter and colleagues are ascribing importance to a child's understanding of the relationship between the mathematical problem and the physical objects, blocks, in this case, and then again a child's understanding of the relationship between the physical objects and the numbers as each are operated on. The emphasis here is on the child's understanding, the meaning that a child makes. There is no particular meaning that a given set of materials is expected to have for all children, or for one child at all times; rather, materials are used by children to sort out their current understandings and to build new ones.

Another group of researchers, Erna Yackel, Paul Cobb, and Terry Wood (1993), present an episode from a second-grade classroom that nicely illustrates different children making different use of the same materials in solving a problem. In this episode, two children are working to figure out what the sum of 12 + 12 + 12 + 12 is. Both children work with Multilink cubes. One child represents each 12 as one stick of ten cubes and two ones.

> She counted up the total as follows, "10, 20, 30, 40, 41, 42, 43, 44, 45, 46, 47, 48." Her partner rejected her method and insisted on counting up by 1's all the way from 12 to 48. For him, each 12 had to be considered as a whole unit and in sequence. His interpretation of the problem, based on his own mathematical construction of numbers, did not include the possibility of finding the sum by partitioning each 12 into 10 and 2 and adding up the four 10's and then the four 2's. (p. 43)

These researchers are particularly interested in the ways that social interaction and communication create opportunities for children to construct more powerful mathematical conceptions. They see situations such as this one, in which two children engage in collaboration, as providing opportunities for both children to learn.

This kind of process, involving physical models[2] and discussion in the context of computation, may help children not only to begin to use groupings of ten, but also to come to deeper understandings of the one-for-ten and ten-for-one trades that can be made at each pair of neighboring places.

Sarah, the third-grade student in Lucy's case 6, provides a wonderful example of a child gaining new insights about tens and ones in this way. We are told that Sarah is able to use the conventional algorithm and can accurately solve two-digit addition problems in other ways as well. In case 6, as she tries to model the conventional algorithm with Unifix cubes, she finds that she has more to understand about carrying the 1. She works at understanding why she arrives at one answer with her block method, in which she moves a stack of 1 ten over to the tens and then counts them as 10 tens, and a different answer with the algorithm, in which the 1 represents a single unit of ten. As a result of this work, she comes to understand something new about the relationship between tens and ones and about the meanings of the places in written number. As Sarah says, "If I put 10 of these up here (pointing to the 10 black cubes attached above the yellow) it equals 1, not just 10" (p. 26). Her use of *just* is interesting. Since 10 is a larger number than 1, she can't mean "a number as small as . . . ," as a child might say, "I have 5 marbles, not just 2." It seems that she has discovered that "ten" can be 1 ten; it isn't "just" 10 ones. This was new to her, and difficult to work out, despite the fact that she was quite able to use the conventional algorithm to calculate the answer. Working to critically examine the reasons that different solution strategies resulted in different answers provided her with a deeper knowledge of the system of tens.

Even after children work out some understanding of the relationship between tens and ones, they still need to learn that, in our number

---

[2] Physical models might be actual objects, as in these examples with Multilink or Unifix cubes. They might also be drawings or diagrams created by a child.

system, ten-for-one and one-for-ten trades can be made at each pair of neighboring places. For each new place, children need to come to understand the value of that place in relation to the other places. Multidigit addition provides a context in which this can happen (Fuson, 1990, 1992).

Multidigit subtraction provides another context for this work. Furthermore, children working on multiunit solutions to subtraction problems also face a complicated set of issues that are not present with addition problems; these create further opportunities for children to elaborate their understandings of how tens and ones are related. With an addition problem, all quantities, no matter how we have broken them apart, are eventually recombined by addition to find the sum: Parts from the different addends can be rearranged to make the calculations convenient. With subtraction, however, as we break apart numbers for easier handling, we must now keep straight which numbers belong to the quantity that is being subtracted, and which belong to the quantity from which we are subtracting. So, for example, if the problem is 64 – 27, any tens-based solution strategy will lead us immediately to issues about how to treat the 4 and the 7.

In Lynn's case 17, "Subtraction and Invented Algorithms," Fiona's work shows us some of the difficulties in keeping track that arise with subtraction; and perhaps these difficulties make the tens-and-ones partitioning of the numbers in the problem less straightforward than it might be for an addition problem using similar numbers. Fiona was working on a word problem, which she represented as 37 – 19. She broke the problem down making use of tens. She first dealt with 30 – 10, then subtracted 9 more (20 – 9 = 11), and then wondered what she needed to do with the 7 that she had dropped from the initial 37. For Fiona, her teacher's question about whether the pigeons stayed or left helped her to sort out what she wanted to do with the 7, and she added it (11 + 7 = 18). Perhaps, though we don't know from a single case, even children who work relatively abstractly and independently of the problem context for addition still rely on a more concrete representation when faced with the complexities of subtraction.

To recap Fiona's solution to this problem, she begins with the tens, subtracting the 10 in 19 from the 30 in 37: 30 – 10 = 20. She then chooses to subtract the 9 ones of 19 from the 2 tens she has left after subtracting 1 ten from 3 tens. The question that she then faces is what operation to perform on the 7 ones that remain to be figured into her calculations. Other solutions highlight other issues.

One step in a solution that many children try is to find the difference between the larger and the smaller number of ones; thus, in the 37 – 19 example, they try 9 – 7 (Kamii, 1989; Wood, 1996). If the problem were an addition problem involving the same quantities (37 + 19), this strategy would not lead us into such complex terrain. We could add 7 + 9 or 9 + 7 to the 3 tens + 1 ten. We would still need to know how the resulting 16 could be combined with the 40, but whether we found it easier to add 7 to 9 or vice versa would not have much impact on the complexity of our work with tens.

This is not so with subtraction. With subtraction, if we decide to deal with the 7 and the 9 by subtracting 7 from 9 (9 – 7 = 2), we are choosing a very complicated solution strategy. In what way can 9 – 7 be a step in an accurate solution to 37 – 19? Subtracting 7 from 9 gives us information about exactly how many ones we need to take from one of the tens of 37. We don't need the whole 10, we need only whatever we can't get from the 7 ones. We need 2 more. So, 30 – 10 = 20, 9 – 7 = 2; we still need to subtract 2 ones from the 2 tens. However, in order to calculate the result of 20 – 2, we must either think about the 20 as 20 ones or as 1 ten + 10 ones; in either case, subtracting 2 ones leaves us with 18.

Students in Emily's case 4 examine a solution to the problem 52 – 28 that relies on these mathematical ideas. One child, Ivan, says, "You take the 20 away from the 50 and get 30. Then you take 8 away from 2, which is –6. Then you take –6 away from 30 and you get 24" (p. 17). Ivan hasn't yet explained why this procedure is a valid and accurate one, but in laying out this solution for consideration, he places himself and his fellow students squarely in front of some important mathematical ideas.

Invented procedures for multiplying and dividing

Breaking apart numbers by tens is an important strategy in multidigit multiplication and division. But for these operations, this decomposition by tens must be done in connection with the distributive property. This presents new challenges.

Children invent procedures for multiplying and dividing, just as they do for adding and subtracting. And, as was the case with addition and subtraction, these computational procedures are opportunities for children to encounter new ideas about units of ten, one hundred, one thousand, and so forth, and to build new understandings. But in the territory of multiplication and division, the issues encountered are different.

Multiplication and division are operations that differ in important ways from addition and subtraction. In both multiplication and division, we are talking about taking a number of same-sized groups, where the number in the group needn't be 1. So, for instance, we can think about 24 groups of 6. If we think about what the 24 and the 6 might be in this example, they describe different levels of organization: one number describes a set (just as all numbers in addition and subtraction do), and the other number describes a set of sets. Let's imagine that the 24 groups of 6 are 24 baskets, each with 6 pieces of fruit in it. The 6 is pieces of fruit, but the 24 is baskets, which in this problem is the same as sets of 6. This is very different from an addition or subtraction situation in which we are talking about having, for example, 24 pieces of fruit and then adding or subtracting 6 other pieces of fruit to or from them. These new uses of number are difficult for children (Hiebert and Behr, 1988).

We can rewrite an addition problem that uses the numbers 24 and 6 to make the comparison with multiplication more accessible: 24 + 6 can be thought of as 24 ones + 6 ones. In the multiplication problem using these numbers, our 24 baskets of 6 pieces of fruit, we now ask for 24 sixes.

475

480

485

490

495

To compute the answer to the multiplication problem, we can collect sets of 6 in different ways and still find the same answer: We can compute 24×6 by first taking 20×6 and then 4×6 and adding the resulting products, or by taking 4×6 and then adding that to 20×6, or by taking 12×6 twice. The property of chunking groups so that, when combined, they form a certain number of sets of a certain size (in this case 24 sets of 6) is called *distributivity*.

While it is convenient to chunk numbers into tens because of our base ten system, and conventional algorithms chunk the multiplication and division processes by place or some power of ten, the value of using tens, hundreds, thousands, and so on in the context of multiplication and division may not be obvious. Again, let's examine what might be involved in solving the problem 24×6, if our solution is to be tens-based. If we stick with our story of having 24 baskets, each with 6 pieces of fruit, one solution that makes use of groupings of ten is to take 2 groups of 10 baskets each, plus the remaining 4 baskets. If we were to write this with numbers, we might write $(10 \times 6) + (10 \times 6) + (4 \times 6)$. If we think about the 24 and 6 as multiunit numbers, keeping in mind the number of each sized unit that each represents, we might write this problem as:

$$(2\,(10) \times 6\,(1)) + (4\,(1) \times 6\,(1))$$

This is not a simple idea to keep in mind, and the complexity only increases as the number of digits in the numbers being multiplied increases.

Currently, there is very little information from researchers that helps us to understand how upper-elementary children think about large numbers, or the relations among powers of ten, and how multiplication and division might affect these. However, it is clear that tens-based solutions are complex even if you are looking for them, and there is good reason to believe that students might not always be looking for them, or thinking in terms of them. Children also make use of other chunks (Lampert, 1986, 1992). We can see this in Eleanor's case 18 in which several children use doubling as a way to solve the problem 4×27. For some, the first strategy was $(2 \times 27) + (2 \times 27)$.

Magdalene Lampert (1992) writes about her work with a fourth-grade class. In their work on division, Lampert asked the children to consider the problem $765 \div 5$. She wanted her instruction to focus on place-value decomposition that would lead students toward an understanding of the steps in the conventional algorithm. To support this focus, Lampert asked the children to consider this problem as making 5 equal-sized groups of money if you have 7 one-hundred-dollar bills, 6 ten-dollar bills, and 5 one-dollar bills. How much money would be in each pile? Children could solve this by imagining dealing out of all of the bills so that in each pile there was 1 one-hundred-dollar bill, 1 ten-dollar bill, and 1 one-dollar bill. Left over were 2 hundreds and 1 ten, which the children then traded for smaller bills so that they could be distributed among the 5 groups. This process emphasized both the 5 same-sized groups and the apportioning of the various hundreds, tens, and ones. It provided a concrete material with which to represent the apportioning carried out numerically in the long division algorithm.

At this time, there is disagreement among researchers and among curriculum developers about the role of the historically-taught computational procedures in a child's mathematics curriculum. What is clear is that when traditionally-taught computational procedures are introduced to children who are still operating primarily with ones or with concrete physical representations, the mapping between the traditional algorithm and the problem is complicated (Kamii, 1993; Lampert, 1986, 1992). Children might learn to perform the steps of these procedures without understanding what each step in the procedure accomplishes or how it relates to their own understanding of the problem.

Let's return to Eleanor's students (case 18) who calculate 4×27 by doubling 27 and doubling again. What work might these students need to do in order to make sense of the conventional algorithm, which asks them first to compute 4×7, write the 8 below the line, then put a 2 over the 2 of 27, then multiply 4×2, add the carried 2 to that product, and write 10 in front of the 8, yielding an answer of 108? Clearly there is a great deal for a person to understand about how the groups are accounted for in this algorithm.

With the traditionally-taught multiplication algorithm children do not at first see how, or if, the algorithm accounts for all the parts that need to be included. For division, it is not clear to children why the long division procedure has them asking, for instance, how many 7s are in 10, when the real question is how many 7s in 109. How the use of groupings based on tens accomplishes these actions is not obvious to children, and therefore is an appropriate focus of instruction (Lampert, 1986, 1992).

Understanding decimal fractions

Decimal fractions share some properties with whole numbers and some with common fractions. Many of the understandings of the system of tens that children build in the domain of whole number serve as important beginnings in their work to make sense of decimals and the kinds of fractional quantities they represent.

Decimal numbers are written with symbols that look like those we use for whole numbers, yet they represent fractional quantities. Decimal fractions indicate values between 0 and 1. So, for instance, no matter how large a decimal fraction we add to the whole number 48, we know that the sum will approach, but never reach, the next whole number 49. The number 48.999999 is still less than one whole unit more than 48.

As with common fractions, between any two decimal fractions there are an infinite number of decimals. Between 1.1 and 1.2, for instance, there are the numbers 1.11 and 1.111 and 1.1111 and so on, as well as 1.12, 1.13, 1.14, . . . We can always add another place to the right that will add smaller and smaller amounts to the original number.

The kinds of fractions represented by decimals are created by successively partitioning the value of one place by ten: Tenths are created by partitioning the unit's value by ten, hundredths are created by partitioning tenths by ten, and so on. This is an important similarity between whole numbers and decimal fractions; as with whole numbers, the relationships between and among places are difficult to sort out and to keep in mind.

There is a relatively large literature on what children don't know how to do with decimals, given traditional instructional methods. Even middle school and high school children have significant difficulty ordering decimals, relating decimals to drawn representations, relating decimals to common fractions, and explaining the rationale for lining up the decimal points for the traditionally-taught addition and subtraction algorithm. (Hiebert, 1992, reviews this literature.)

575

580

585

590

595

Many researchers believe that these difficulties are not surprising. Several lines of evidence suggest that human beings very naturally, and from a very early age, whether schooled or not (e.g., Carraher, Schliemann, & Carraher, 1988), first think of numbers as what we get when we count things. Fractions, however, are not what we get from a simple counting. They result from dividing one quantity by another, and this notion of number may not come to people as intuitively or as easily (Gelman, Cohen, & Hartnett, 1989).

Many of the errors that children make when working with decimals suggest that they are applying whole-number rules and procedures to decimal numbers. Two examples from research follow. A ninth grader writes 5.1 directly underneath .36 and says, "If you're adding .36 and 5.1 it would make a lot more sense if it came out to .8 or so" (Hiebert and Wearne, 1986). More than half of all 13-year-olds in the U.S. are unable to correctly choose the largest among .19, .036, .195, and .2 (Carpenter, Corbitt, Kepner, Lindquist, & Reys, 1981). Many of these children select .195 as the largest number, as it would be if the decimal point were removed.

Similar findings are reported by Lauren Resnick and her colleagues (1989). They conducted a study of 113 American, French, and Israeli fourth, fifth, and sixth graders, children who were in the early phases of their school work on decimals. These researchers were interested in whether or not children's interpretations of decimals could be described as being consistent with underlying rules. The rules of most interest to them were the *whole-number rule* and the *fraction rule*. According to the whole-number rule, children judge one decimal to be larger than another when it has more decimal places, as would be true of whole-number comparisons. Thus, children whose judgments are consistent with the whole-number rule would correctly say that .64 is larger than .2, but would incorrectly say that .64 is larger than .8. Resnick and her colleagues also reasoned that some children base their decimal comparisons on their knowledge of common fractions, particularly their knowledge that the more parts a whole is divided into, the smaller the parts. These children's judgments might be consistent with the fraction rule. According to this rule, more decimal places indicate parts of smaller size and lead to judgments that seem not to take account of how many of those smaller-sized pieces are being denoted. These children would correctly judge .64 to be smaller than .8, but would incorrectly judge .64 also to be smaller than .2.

By asking children to make a variety of judgments of this kind and through other interview questions about decimals, Resnick and her coworkers found that, to a very high degree, children's responses either were consistent with one of these two rules (or with a less common variant of the whole-number rule—children treated decimals with a zero in the tenths place as a special case), or were correct for all items.

This research makes very clear that (1) in the United States, the whole-number-rule pattern is the most commonly occurring error pattern among children who are just beginning to work with decimals, and (2) children are making sense of the decimal-fraction system by trying to connect it with the kind of number system of which they already have some working knowledge. This productive strategy also leads to errors; these errors are an important source of information to a teacher, and a source of discussion and new opportunities for learning for the class.

In Nicole's case 28, we see children making judgments similar to those that a whole-number rule would generate. A group of children working on a word problem about a jeweler and grams of gold add 1.14, .089, and .3 by aligning them on the right as they would for whole numbers, arriving at an answer of 2.06. A little later in the class discussion, one of the children in this group asserts that another child's answer of 1.529 is too big. He believes that 1.529 is larger than his own answer of 2.06. For him, it is as if the decimal points are not there and these numbers are to be treated as whole numbers.

Kathryn Irwin's (1996) research with 11- and 12-year-old students provides some detailed illustration of the complexity of children's work in sorting out which aspects of their whole-number knowledge apply to decimal fractions and which must be adapted. Irwin reports on one pair of students who are considering the question, Is one hundredth written as .100 or as .01? The students thought that .100 looked right, but they also knew that the number .355 was called 355 thousandths, and it didn't make sense to them that .100 would be hundredths if .355 was thousandths. These children also wondered if there were a "oneths" column. If .100 were to be the way to write one hundredth, then, they reasoned, there needed to be a oneths column, along with the tenths and hundredths columns. The children that Irwin observed were working hard to understand the written-number system as it applied to whole numbers and decimal fractions. Their questions about how to write the numbers belie their questions about the meanings and values of the places to the right of the decimal point and how these values are related to whole-number values.

The work of James Hiebert, Diana Wearne, and Susan Taber (1991) begins to show some of what it takes for students to go beyond these initial conceptions. Hiebert and his colleagues studied one classroom of fourth-grade children, for whom they provided 11 days of decimal-fraction study. Their instruction was aimed at using concrete, physical representations to help children develop clearer meanings for tenths, hundredths, and so on. As a result of their intervention, Hiebert et al. found that children became more and more likely to offer correct, quantitative interpretations of decimals, to represent decimal fractions with concrete materials, and to make correct comparisons among different decimal numbers.

Returning to Nicole's case 28, in which children are working to add the numbers 1.14, .089, and .3, we see children doing work very similar to that reported by Hiebert et al. (1991). They call upon their understandings of the numbers—and the different places—to decide how to add, explaining the reason they didn't line up all the numbers was that "we needed to line up the tenths with the tenths and the hundredths with the hundredths to make it come out right." In order to convince their classmates, and themselves, children represented the decimal quantities with blocks. The children, including those who had initially solved the problem incorrectly, were intrigued, and continued to make up new problems to solve as they worked further to understand the mathematics of these numbers.

We saw earlier in this essay how much work children must do in order to sort out the relationship between ones and tens in whole numbers and to stay mindful of this relationship while working with multidigit numbers. The issue is no less complex in the case of decimal fractions; children must keep in mind that one tenth is both 1 tenth and 10 hundredths. Nor is it the case that these children, who years before sorted out at least some aspects of these tens relations for whole numbers, can in some quick and simple way transfer that understanding to the quantities represented by the infinite number of places we can create to the right of the decimal point. What we do know to be true is this: By building on their earlier understandings of whole number in the base ten system, children come to know what decimal fractions mean and gain some sense of the power and elegance of the decimal system.

Conclusion

The ideas that children confront as they try to make sense of place value are very complex. We know more about the development of children's understandings of some of these ideas than we do about others. Perhaps we know least about children's understandings of large numbers and the effects of multiplication and division on powers of ten. With respect to any of the five themes examined here, however, we are all still learning about the ideas that children begin with, and how they come to build stronger conceptions. We move toward a clearer picture of this as teachers and researchers continue to make public their thoughtful and careful observations of children building a system of tens.

715

720

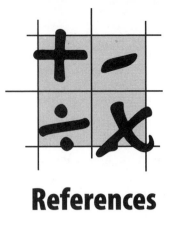

References

Behr, M. (1976). *Teaching experiment: The effect of manipulatives in second-graders' learning of mathematics* (PMDC Technical Report No. 11). Tallahassee: Florida State University. (ERIC Document Reproduction Service No. ED 144 809)

Beishuizen, M. (1993). Mental strategies and materials or models for addition and subtraction up to 100 in Dutch second grades. *Journal for Research in Mathematics Education, 24*, 294–323.

Bell, J., & Burns, J. (1981). Counting and numeration capabilities of primary school children: A preliminary report. In T. R. Post & M. P. Roberts (Eds.), *Proceedings of the Third Annual Meeting of the North American Chapter of the International Group for the Psychology of Mathematics Education* (pp. 17–23). Minneapolis: University of Minnesota.

Burns, M. (1987). *A collection of math lessons from grades 3 through 6.* Sausalito, CA: Math Solutions Publications.

Carpenter, T. P., Corbitt, M. K., Kepner, H. S., Lindquist, M. M., & Reys, R. E. (1981). Decimals: Results and implications from the second NAEP mathematics assessment. *Arithmetic Teacher, 28* (8), 34–37.

Carpenter, T. P., Fennema, E., & Franke, M. L. (1996). Cognitively Guided Instruction: A knowledge base for reform in primary mathematics instruction. *Elementary School Journal 97* (1), 3–20.

Carraher, T. N., Schliemann, A. D., & Carraher, D. W. (1988). Mathematical concepts in everyday life. In G. B. Saxe & M. Gearhart (Eds.), *New Directions for Child Development*, No. 41. San Francisco: Jossey-Bass.

Cobb, P. (1995). Cultural tools and mathematical learning: A case study. *Journal for Research in Mathematics Education, 26*, 362–385.

Cobb, P., & Wheatley, G. (1988). Children's initial understandings of ten. *Focus on Learning Problems in Mathematics, 10*, 1–28.

Fuson, K. C. (1990). Conceptual structures for multiunit numbers: Implications for learning and teaching multidigit addition, subtraction, and place-value. *Cognition and Instruction, 7,* 343–404.

Fuson, K. C. (1992). Research on learning and teaching addition and subtraction of whole numbers. In G. Leinhardt, R. Putnam, & R. A. Hattrup (Eds.), *Analysis of arithmetic for mathematics teaching* (pp. 53–187). Hillsdale, NJ: Erlbaum.

Gelman, R., Cohen, M., & Hartnett, P. (1989). To know mathematics is to go beyond thinking that "fractions aren't numbers." *Proceedings of the Eleventh Annual Meeting of the North American Chapter of the International Group for the Psychology of Mathematics Education* (pp. 29–67). New Brunswick, NJ: Rutgers University.

Hiebert, J. (1992). Mathematical, cognitive, and instructional analyses of decimal fractions. In G. Leinhardt, R. Putnam, & R. A. Hattrup (Eds.), *Analysis of arithmetic for mathematics teaching* (pp. 283–322). Hillsdale, NJ: Erlbaum.

Hiebert, J. & Behr, M. (1988). Introduction. In J. Hiebert & M. Behr (Eds.), *Number concepts and operations in the middle grades* (pp. 1–18). Hillsdale, NJ and Reston, VA: Lawrence Erlbaum Associates and National Council of Teachers of Mathematics.

Hiebert, J., & Wearne, D., (1986). Procedures over concepts: The acquisition of decimal number knowledge. In J. Hiebert (Ed.), *Conceptual and procedural knowledge: The case of mathematics* (pp. 199–223). Hillsdale, NJ: Erlbaum.

Hiebert, J., Wearne, D., & Taber, S. (1991). Fourth-graders' gradual construction of decimal fractions during instruction using different physical representations. *The Elementary School Journal, 91* (4), 321–341.

Irwin, K. (1996, April). *Why are decimal fractions difficult?* Paper presented at the Annual Meeting of the American Educational Research Association, New York.

Kamii, C. (1989). *Young children continue to reinvent arithmetic—2nd grade: Implications of Piaget's theory.* New York: Teachers College Press.

Kamii, C. (1993). *Young children continue to reinvent arithmetic—3rd grade: Implications of Piaget's theory.* New York: Teachers College Press.

Kamii, C., Lewis, B. A., & Livingston, S. J. (1993). Primary arithmetic: Children inventing their own procedures. *Arithmetic Teacher, 41,* 200–203.

Lampert, M. (1986). Knowing, doing, and teaching multiplication. *Cognition and Instruction, 3*, 305–342.

Lampert, M. (1992). Teaching and learning long division for understanding in school. In G. Leinhardt, R. Putnam, & R. A. Hattrup (Eds.), *Analysis of arithmetic for mathematics teaching* (pp. 221–282). Hillsdale, NJ: Erlbaum.

Madell, R. (1985). Children's natural processes. *Arithmetic Teacher, 32* (7), 20–22.

Resnick, L. B. (1992). From protoquantities to operators: Building mathematical competence on a foundation of everyday knowledge. In G. Leinhardt, R. Putnam, & R. A. Hattrup (Eds.), *Analysis of arithmetic for mathematics teaching* (pp. 373–429). Hillsdale, NJ: Erlbaum.

Resnick, L. B., Lesgold, S., & Bill, V. (1990, July). *From protoquantities to number sense.* Paper presented at the International Group for the Psychology of Mathematics Education, Mexico City.

Resnick, L. B., Nesher, P., Leonard, F., Magone, M., Omanson, S., & Peled, I. (1989). Conceptual bases of arithmetic errors: The case of decimal fractions. *Journal for Research in Mathematics Education, 20* (1), 8–27.

Ross, S. (1989). Parts, wholes, and place value: A developmental view. *Arithmetic Teacher, 36* (6), 47–51.

Sitomer, M. (1978) *Zero is not nothing.* New York: Harper Crest.

Steffe, L. (1988). Children's construction of number sequences and multiplying schemes. In J. Hiebert & M. Behr (Eds.), *Number concepts and operations in the middle grades* (pp. 119–140). Hillsdale, NJ, and Reston, VA: Erlbaum and National Council of Teachers of Mathematics.

Steffe, L. P., Cobb, P., & Von Glasersfeld, E. (1988). *Construction of arithmetical meanings and strategies.* New York: Springer-Verlag.

Van de Walle, J. A. (1990) *Elementary school mathematics: Teaching developmentally.* White Plains, NY: Longman.

Wood, T. (1996). Events in learning mathematics: Insights from research in classrooms. *Educational Studies in Mathematics, 30*, 85–105.

Yackel, E., Cobb, P., & Wood, T. (1993). Developing a basis for mathematical communication within small groups [monograph]. *Journal for Research in Mathematics Education*, 33–44.